Complete Solutions Manual for Introduction to DISCRETE MATHEMATICS

R. Hirschfelder
University of Puget Sound

J. Hirschfelder
Honeywell, Inc.

Brooks/Cole Publishing Company
Pacific Grove, California

Brooks/Cole Publishing Company
A Division of Wadsworth, Inc.

Printed in the United States of America

5 4 3 2 1

ISBN 0-534-13897-7

Preface

This manual contains solutions to all exercises in the text, both odd-numbered and even-numbered, exclusive of the computer exercises. The table of contents provides Chapter and Section numbers of the answers.

Once again, we would like to thank Chuck Hommel of the University of Puget Sound for his careful checking of all solutions. Thanks also to Discrete Mathematics students at the University of Puget Sound who provided some of the solutions, especially Della Sparks, Shawnell Stevens, Lisa Mancuso, and Bob Chapman.

Contents

COMPLETE SOLUTIONS MANUAL

for

INTRODUCTION TO DISCRETE MATHEMATICS

Chapter 1

Section 1.1

1. a) 10001 b) 10000000000 c) 11100100 d) 101010111100

2. a) 100000000 b) 1100100 c) 1000010 d) 1001010110

3. a) 14711 b) 31 c) 38 d) 57005

4. a) 511 b) 57 c) 170 d) 2766

5. a) 174 b) 7C

6. a) 746 b) 1F4

7. a) 1221 b) 291

8. a) 241605 b) 2870

9. a) not prime b) prime c) not prime d) prime

10. a) prime b) not prime c) not prime d) not prime

Section 1.2

1. a) 110100 b) 110010

2. a) 100010010 b) 110000

3. a) 1000111111 b) 1110111111

4. a) 1011011001 b) 1000010

5. 100010

6. 110011

7. a) 4344 b) 46

8. a) 701 b) 3065

9. a) 79BDF b) BC836

10. a) 119B60 b) FEDCBA

11. No. Suppose b is the base and $b \geq 2$. Then if b-1 is a digit in base b, $(b - 1)(b - 1) > b - 1$ and therefore, there will be a carry.

12. If A is the length of the dividend, B is the length of the divisor, LQ is the length of the quotient, and LR is the length of the remainder, then either $LQ = A - B$ or $LQ = A - B + 1$ and $0 \leq LR \leq B$.

13. YYY YYYY <<<<

14. <YYY

Section 1.3

1. a) $x_8^2 + x_9^2 + \dots + x_{20}^2$

   b) $(x_1 + y_1)^2 + (x_2 + y_2)^2 + \dots + (x_{10} + y_{10})^2$

   c) $x_1^2 + y_1^2 + x_2^2 + y_2^2 + \dots + x_{10}^2 + y_{10}^2$

   d) 225 e) 39 f) 66

2. a) 385 b) 3025 c) 612 d) 1200 e) 9 f) 126

3. a) $\sum_{i=5}^{22} i$ b) $\sum_{i=1}^{20} x_i$

4. a) $\sum_{i=0}^{50} 2i$ b) $\sum_{i=1}^{n} x_i y_i$

5. a)
$$\sum_{i=1}^{n} (x_i + 5) = \sum_{i=1}^{n} x_i + \sum_{i=1}^{n} 5 \qquad \text{(rule 3)}$$
$$= \sum_{i=1}^{n} x_i + 5n \qquad \text{(rule 1)}$$

6. a) $y_8\, y_9\, y_{10} \dots y_{15}$

   b) $(x_1 + y_1)(x_2 + y_2) \dots (x_5 + y_5)$

7. a) $(x + 2)^2 (x + 4)^2 \dots (x + 20)^2$ b) 0

8. a) $\sum_{i=0}^{14} (i + 1)^2$ b) $\sum_{k=3}^{8} k^3$

9. a) $\sum_{i=1}^{10} 1/i^2$ b) $\sum_{k=1}^{6} (k + 3)^2$

10. $(1^1 + 1^2 + 1^3) + (2^1 + 2^2 + 2^3) + (3^1 + 3^2 + 3^3) = 295$

11. $(0 + 0)(0 + 1)(0 + 2)(0 + 3) + (1 + 0)(1 + 1)(1 + 2)(1 + 3)$
$+ (2 + 0)(2 + 1)(2 + 2)(2 + 3) = 144$

12. c^{n-k+1}

Section 1.4

1. 2 2. 0 3. 30.8125

4. 17.4375 5. $10011.\overline{0011}$ 6. $11.01\overline{1100}$

7. Convert integer part as before. To convert fractional part, use successive multiplication by 8 until the fractional part is zero or the pattern repeats. Then write down the integer part from top to bottom.

   a) 3.4 b) $14.2\overline{3146}$ c) 0.2 d) $7.\overline{0050753412172702436 56}$

8. a) 0.74174 b) 0.7470 c) 0.06506

9. a) 0.F0F8 b) 0.C00B c) 0.1FF8

10. a) Let x = 0.5 and y = 0.4999... Then

$$x = 5/10 = 1/2 \quad \text{and } y = 450/900 = 1/2 = x$$

Section 1.5

1. Assume √3 is rational and deduce a contradiction using the method shown in the text for the case of √2.

2. Assume $\log_2 5 = p/q$ where p/q is a non-zero fraction in lowest terms. Then

$$2^{p/q} = 5 \quad \text{and}$$

$$(2^{p/q})^q = 5^q \quad \text{so that}$$

$$2^p = 5^q \quad \text{which is not true for non-zero values of p and q.}$$

3.

Imaginary axis

$1+7i$

$-3+2.5i$

$2.2i$

-3.5

Real axis

1.8

$-2.5-i$

$-1.2i$

$3-5i$

4. a) $13 + 43i$ b) $21.1 - 92.6i$ c) $8-2i$

   d) $-3 + 4i$ e) $-i$

5. a) $0.06 - 12.15i$ b) $-2 + 262i$

   c) $82 + 58i$ d) 1 e) 1

6. a) $\sqrt{34}$, 59° b) $\sqrt{34}$, 301° c) $\sqrt{34}$, 121°

   d) $\sqrt{34}$, 239° e) 4, 180° f) 1, 270°

7. a) $1.06 + 0.75i$ b) $-2.46 + 0.43i$

   c) $-i$ d) $-1.88 + 0.68i$

8. a) $-1-i$, $1/(1+i) = (1-i)/2$

   b) $-1+2i$, $1/(1-2i) = (1+2i)/5$

   c) $5i$, $i/5$ d) $3-i$, $1/(-3+i) = (-3-i)/10$

   e) 4, $-1/4$ f) $2+\sqrt{2}i$, $1/(-2-\sqrt{2}i) = (-2+\sqrt{2}i)/6$

9. a) $2 - 3i$ b) $-6 + 7$ c) 17 d) $-2.2i$

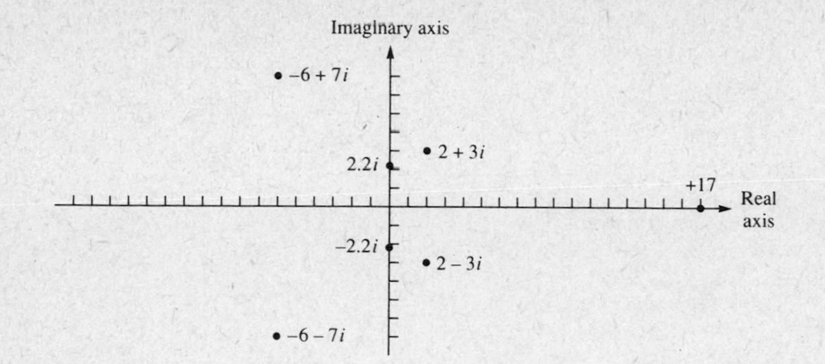

10. Let $z = a + bi$. Then

a)

$$z\bar{z} = (a + bi)(a - bi)$$
$$= a^2 + b^2$$
$$= [\sqrt{(a^2 + b^2)}]^2$$
$$= |z|^2$$

b) Real part $(z) = a = [(a + bi) + (a - bi)]/2 = (z + \bar{z})/2$

c) Imaginary part $(z) = b = [(a + bi) - (a - bi)]/2i$

$$= (z - \bar{z})/2$$

11. a) $(18 + i)/25$ b) $(4.5 - 2i)/24.25$

c) $(13 - 84i)/85$ d) $(1 - i)/2$

12. a) $(-1 \pm \sqrt{3}i)/2$ b) $(7 \pm \sqrt{7}i)/4$

c) $\pm \sqrt{3}i$ d) $3, -4$ e) 3 f) $(-1 \pm \sqrt{3}i)/2, 0$

The solutions are symmetric about the real axis.

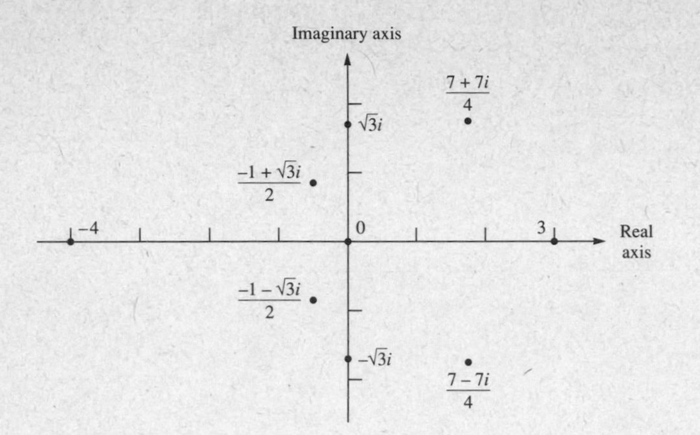

13. Use the method of exercise 2, with 2 replaced by p. The proof uses only the fact that if a prime p divides x^2, then p divides x.

14. It suffices to show that $|z|^2|w|^2 = |zw|^2$. Let $z = x + iy$ and $w = a + ib$. Then $|z|^2 = x^2 + y^2$ and $|w|^2 = a^2 + b^2$. Also, $zw = (ax - by) + i(bx + ay)$ so that $|zw|^2 = (ax - by)^2 + (bx + ay)^2$. It can now be verified by algebra that this is equal to $(x^2 + y^2)(a^2 + b^2)$.

15. By definition of cosine and sine, $\cos(\arg(z)) = a/|z|$, and $\sin(\arg(z)) = b/|z|$.

16. Let $z = a + bi$, $w = c + di$, $\Theta = \operatorname{Arg}(z)$, and $\phi = \operatorname{Arg}(w)$. By the previous exercise $a = |z|\cos\Theta$ and $b = |z|\sin\Theta$, so that

$$\begin{aligned} z &= |z|\cos\Theta + i|z|\sin\Theta \\ &= |z|(\cos\Theta + i\sin\Theta) \end{aligned}$$

Similarly, $w = |w|(\cos\phi + i\sin\phi)$. Then

$$\begin{aligned} zw &= |zw|[(\cos\Theta\cos\phi - \sin\Theta\sin\phi) + i(\cos\Theta\cos\phi + \sin\Theta\sin\phi)] \\ &= |z||w|[\cos(\Theta+\phi) + i\sin(\Theta+\phi)] \end{aligned}$$

Thus, $\Theta+\phi$ is the argument of zw.

Section 1.6

1. a) 59, 59 b) 177, -79 c) 239, -17

2. a) 00000010, carry   b) 11111111, neither

c) 11001001, neither   d) 01100110, carry

3. a) -2^{15} to $2^{15} - 1$ b) -2^{31} to $2^{31} - 1$

4. a) 0, 1 b) 2, 3

5. a) 7864 b) -8145

6. Add 1 to the one's complement negative.

7. a) T b) T c) F

8. a) T b) F c) F

9. a) [1], [3], [5], [7], [9], [11], [13], [15]

b) [1], [2], [3], [4], [5], [6]

10. a) [1], [2], [4], [7], [8], [11], [13], [14]

b) [1], [2], [3], [4]

11. If $[a] = [a']$ and $[b] = [b']$, then $a - a' = kn$ and $b - b' = hn$. So

$$\begin{aligned} ab - a'b' &= ab - a'b + a'b - a'b' \\ &= (a - a')b + a'(b - b') \\ &= (kn)b + a'(hn) \\ &= n(kb + a'h) \end{aligned}$$

Therefore, $[ab] = [a'b']$.

12. a) 30 b) -14   c) -121

13. a) 01111001, carry and overflow   b) 00011110, carry

c) 00010101, carry   d) 10111101, overflow

14. Assume the word length is N bits, and let the summands be A and B. Interpret A and B as nonnegative integers: $0 \le A \le 2^N$, $0 \le B \le 2^N - 1$. There is an end-around carry if $A + B \ge 2^N$. But the carry is added to $A + B - 2^N$, and $A + B \le 2^N + 2^N - 2$. So $A + B - 2^N \le 2^N - 2$. After adding the carry, the sum is at most

$(2^N - 2) + 1 = 2^N - 1$, so there is no further carry.

15. The two's complement negative is 1 plus the one's complement negative.

16. $z^j z^k = z^{j+k}$. If $j + k \leq n - 1$, then $z^{j+k} \in X$. Otherwise, $z^{j+k} = z^{j+k-n} \in X$ since $z^n = 1$.

Chapter Review

1. a) 111001 b) 71 c) 39
2. a) 100000 b) 40 c) 20
3. a) 63 b) 12 c) 108
4. a) 174 b) 30 c) 61453
5. a) 3424 b) 714
6. a) 101010111 b) 111001011
7. 272
8. 220212
9. a) not prime b) not prime c) not prime d) prime
10. a) 111000 b) 1101001 c) 1101110
11. Use the method of Exercise 2, Section 1.5.
12.

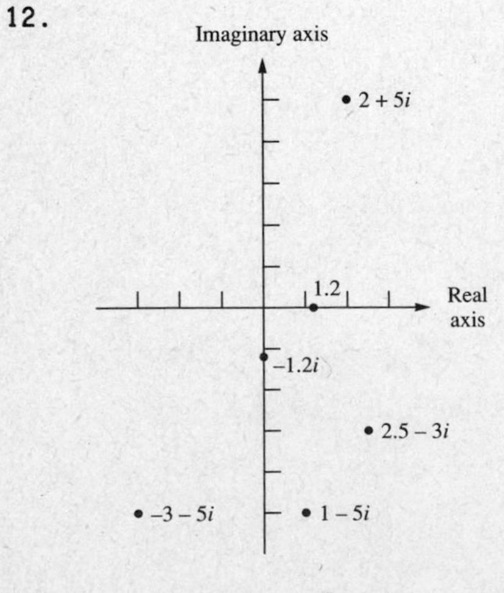

13. a) 3 + 10i b) –2 + 28i

14. a) $17 + i$ b) $36 + 8i$ c) $-5 + 2i$ d) 2

e) $-i$ f) -1

15. a) $\sqrt{13}, 34^\circ$ b) $\sqrt{29}, -68^\circ$ c) $\sqrt{17}, 166^\circ$

d) $\sqrt{13}, -124^\circ$ e) $5, 180^\circ$ f) $2, 270^\circ$

16. a) $1.04 + 0.6i$ b) $0.48 + 0.15i$ c) $1 - 1.73i$

d) $2.5 + 4.33i$

17. a) $-1-2i, (1-2i)/5$ b) $-2+2i, (1+i)/4$ c) $3i, i/3$

d) $4-i, (-4-i)/17$ e) $8, -1/8$ f) $1-\sqrt{2}i, (-1-\sqrt{2}i)/3$

18. 65536

19. a) 1111100111011011 b) 1111100111011100

20. a) 61 b) -3

21. a) 61 b) -4

22. a) 01101010, carry and overflow b) 00001110, carry

c) 10111011, overflow d) 10101011, carry

e) 01110111, carry

23. a) 01101001, carry and overflow b) 00001101, carry

c) 10111011, overflow d) 10101010, carry

e) 01110110, carry

24. a) 3.625 b) 7.1875

25. a) $1100.\overline{0110}$ b) $111.\overline{0001011110000101000111}$

26. a) T b) F c) F d) F e) F f) F

27. a) [1], [3], [5], [7]

b) [1], [3], [7], [9]

28. $[(3 - 2(5)) + (3 - 2(6))][(4 - 2(5)) + (4 - 2(6))] = 182$

29. $(1^1 2^1 3^1)(1^2 2^2 3^2)(1^3 2^3 3^3) = 46{,}656$

Chapter 2

Section 2.1

1. a) $B \not\subset C$ b) $r \in C$ c) $m \notin B$

   d) $C \subset A$ e) $\phi \subset B$ f) $B \subset B$

2. a) F b) F c) T d) F e) F f) F

3. a) { 1, 2, 3, 4, 5, 6, 7, 8, 9, 10 }

   b) { 3, 6, 9, 12, ... } c) { -2, -1, 0, 1, 2 }

   d) { 1, 1/2, 1/3, 1/4, ... }

   e) { 2, 4, 8, 16, ... } f) { -4, 4 } g) { -1, 1 }

4. a) $\{ n^2 \mid n \in N \}$ b) $\{ n \mid n \in Z \text{ and } n > 5 \}$

   c) $\{ 2n \mid n \in N \}$

   d) $\{ n \mid n \in N,\ n < 20, \text{ and } n \text{ is prime} \}$

5. a) $C \subset D$

6. $A = B$ and $C = \phi$

7. Since $A \subset B$, if $x \in A$, then $x \in B$ and $x \in C$ since $B \subset C$.

   Thus, $A \subset C$.

8. Nothing

9. $A \subset B$, $B \not\subset A$

10. $$\sum_{\substack{-101<n<101 \\ n \text{ even}}} n^2$$

11. $$\sum_{x_i \in S} x_i$$

12. $$\sum_{w_i \in M} w_i$$

Section 2.2

1. a) B b) { e, r } c) { c, o, r, e, t, m } d) B

   e) { m, p, u, t } f) { t, m } g) ϕ h) { c, o }

   i) { p, u } j) { m, p, u, t, r, e }

   k) { c, o, m, p, u, t } l) { c, o }

2. a) { 1 } b) { 1 } c) C d) { 1 }

   e) { 0, 1, 3, 4, 5, 6, 7 } f) { 0, 4, 6 }

g) { 1, 2, 3, 5, 7 } h) { 3, 5, 7 } i) D' j) D

3. a) { 20, 22, 24, ... , 36 }

   b) { 19, 21, 23, 25, 27, 29, 31, 33, 35 }

   c) { 2, 4, 6, ... , 18 }

   d) { 2, 4, 6, ... , 18, 19, 20, 21, ... , 36 }

4. a) ϕ b) { 10, 20, 30, ... } c) ϕ d) ϕ e) { 1 }

   f) { 1 }

5. a) B b) B c) { a, b, {a}, {a,b} } d) B

   e) { {a}, {a,b} } f) { {a,b} }

6. A = { 1, 2 }, B = { 2, 3 }, and C = { 1, 4 }

7. No since $A \cap B \cap C$ is a subset of $A \cap B$, $A \cap C$, and $B \cap C$.

8. A = ϕ, B = { ϕ }, and C = { B }

9. { ϕ, {a}, {b}, {c}, {a,b}, {a,c}, {b,c}, A }

10. { ϕ, {a}, { {a} }, A }

11. { ϕ, {ϕ}, {A}, P(A) }

12. a) { ϕ, a, {a} } b) ϕ c) P(A)

    d) { A } e) P(A) f) { ϕ }

13. a) { 0, 2, 5, 6, 7, 9 } b) { 1, 2, 4, 5, 7, 9 }

    c) { 0, 2, 5, 6, 7 } d) { 1, 3, 4, 9 }

    e) A f) ϕ

14. a) { ... −3, −2, −1, 0 } b) set of irrationals

15.

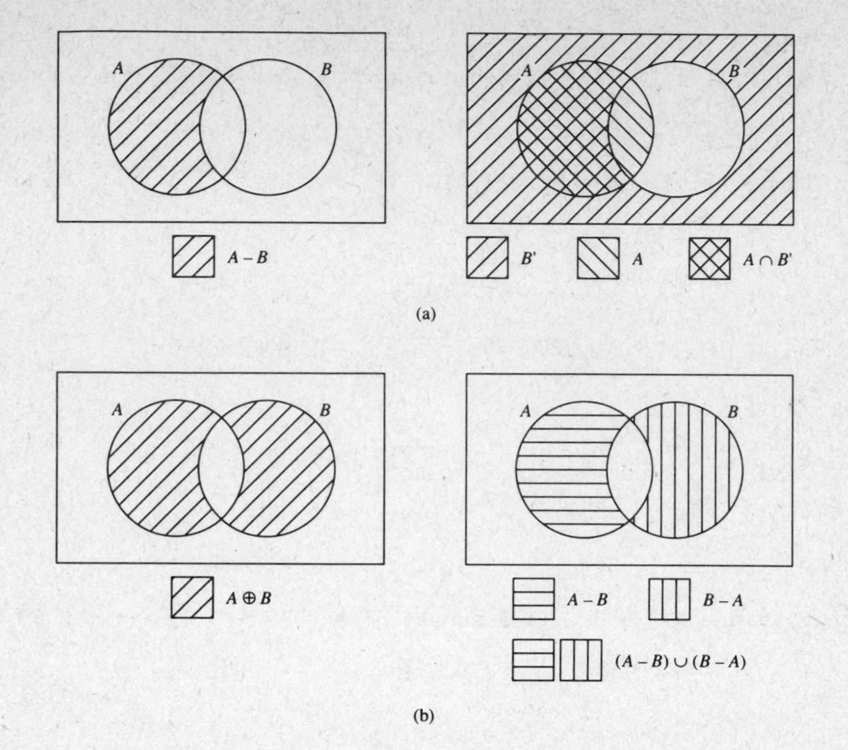

(a)

(b)

16. a) If $x \in (A \cap B)'$, then $x \notin A \cap B$ so either $x \notin A$ or $x \notin B$. If $x \notin A$, then $x \in A'$, and if $x \notin B$, then $x \in B'$. So $x \in A' \cup B'$, hence, $(A \cap B)' \subset A' \cup B'$. If $x \in A' \cup B'$, then $x \in A'$ or $x \in B'$. If $x \in A'$, then $x \notin A$, and so $x \notin A \cap B$. If $x \in B'$, then $x \notin B$, and so $x \notin A \cap B$, and, therefore, $x \in (A \cap B)'$. So $A' \cup B' \subset (A \cap B)'$.

b) If $x \in (A')'$, then $x \notin A'$, so $x \in A$ and $(A')' \subset A$. If $x \in A$, then $x \notin A'$, so $x \in (A')'$ and $A \subset (A')'$.

c) If $x \in A \cap (B \cup C)$, then $x \in A$ and $x \in B \cup C$. If $x \in B \cup C$, then $x \in B$ or $x \in C$. If $x \in B$, then $x \in A \cap B$, and if $x \in C$, then $x \in A \cap C$. So $x \in (A \cap B) \cup (A \cap C)$. If $x \in (A \cap B) \cup (A \cap C)$, then $x \in A \cap B$ or $x \in A \cap C$. If $x \in A \cap B$, then $x \in A$, and if $x \in A \cap C$, then $x \in A$. So $x \in A$ in either case, and either $x \in B$ or $x \in C$ in addition. Therefore, $x \in A \cap (B \cup C)$.

17. a) If $x \in (A - B)'$, then $x \notin A - B$, so either $x \notin A$ or $x \in B$, that is, $x \in A' \cup B$. So $(A - B)' \subset A' \cup B$. If $x \in A' \cup B$, then either $x \in A'$ or $x \in B$. If $x \in B$, then $x \notin A - B$, so $x \in (A - B)'$. If $x \in A'$, then $x \notin A$, so $x \notin A - B$, and $x \in (A - B)'$.

b) If $x \in A \cap (A \cup B)$, then $x \in A$ so $A \cap (A \cup B) \subset A$. If $x \in A$, then $x \in A \cup B$, so $x \in A \cap (A \cup B)$, and $A \subset A \cap (A \cup B)$.

18. Suppose that $B' \not\subset A$. Then there is an element x, such that $x \in B'$ and $x \notin A$. So $x \in A'$. But $A' = B$ so that $x \in B$ contradicting the assumption that $x \in B'$.

19. a) If $x \in A \oplus B$, then exactly one of the following holds:

(1) $x \in A$, $x \notin B$, $x \in C$; then $x \in B \oplus C$

(2) $x \in A$, $x \notin B$, $x \notin C$; then $x \in A \oplus C$

(3) $x \notin A$, $x \in B$, $x \in C$; then $x \in A \oplus C$

(4) $x \notin A$, $x \in B$, $x \notin C$; then $x \in B \oplus C$

b) If $A \oplus B = \phi$, then $A \cup B = A \cap B$, so $A = B$.

c) If $x \in A \oplus B$, then either:

(1) $x \in A$ and $x \notin B$; then $x \notin A'$ and $x \in B'$

(2) $x \in B$ and $x \notin A$; then $x \notin B'$ and $x \in A'$

This shows $A \oplus B \subset A' \oplus B'$. Converse is similar.

d) Similar to (c); check each of eight cases.

20. a) False, $A = \{1, 2\}$, $B = \{2, 3\}$, $X = \{0, 1, 2, 3\}$

b) False, counterexample same as for part a)

c) True. If $C \subset A$ and $C \subset B$ then $C \subset A \cap B$ and conversely.

d) False, counterexample same as for part a)

21. a) False; A, B, X same as for part a) of Problem 20, and $C = \{3\}$.

b) False; A, B, X same as for part a) of Problem 20, and

$C = \{ 0, 2, 3 \}$

c) True. If $x \in A$, then $x \in A \cup B$, so $x \in A \cap B$, therefore

$x \in B$. This shows that $A \subset B$. Similarly $B \subset A$.

d) True. If $x \in A \cup C$, then either $x \in A$ or $x \in C$. If

$x \in A$, then $x \in B$ since $A \subset B$, so $x \in B \cup D$. If $x \in C$,

then $x \in D$ since $C \subset D$, so $x \in B \cup D$. So $A \cup C \subset B \cup D$.

Section 2.3

1. $\{ 1, 2, 3 \}$

2. a) $[-3,-1]$ b) $(-\infty,-2)$ c) $[7,\infty)$

3. a) $[0,\infty)$ b) $(-3,-2) \cup (2,3)$

4. a) F b) T c) F d) T

5. a) F b) F c) F d) F

6. a) $(-2,1)$ b) $(3,5)$ c) $[-1,4)$

   d) $(-5,0)$ e) ϕ

7. a) $\{ 1 \}$ b) $(-\infty,1]$ c) $(-\infty,1] \cup \{ 2 \}$

   d) $(0,1) \cup (1,3)$ e) $(1,4]$

8. a) $(4,\infty)$ b) $(-\infty,0) \cup (1,\infty)$

9. a) $(-\infty,0] \cup [1,\infty)$ b) $(-\infty,-5]$

Section 2.4

1. a) $\{ (1,0), (1,1), (2,0), (2,1), (3,0), (3,1), (4.0),$
   $(4,1) \}$

   b) $\{ (0,1), (0,2), (0,3), (0,4), (1,1), (1,2), (1,3),$
   $(1,4) \}$

   c) $\{ (0,0), (0,1), (1,0), (1,1) \}$

d) $\{ \phi, \{(0,0)\}, \{(0,1)\}, \{(1,0)\}, \{(1,1)\}, \{(0,0),(0,1)\},$

$\{(0,0),(1,0)\}, \{(0,0),(1,1)\}, \{(0,1),(1,0)\},$

$\{(0,1),(1,1)\},\{(1,0),(1,1)\},\{(0,0),(0,1),(1,0)\},$

$\{(0,0),(0,1),(1,1)\}, \{(0,0),(1,0),(1,1)\},$

$\{(0,1),(1,0),(1,1)\}, B \times B \}$

2. $\{ (1,1), (1,2), (1,3), (3,1), (2,1), (2,2) \}$

3. $\{ (1,2), (1,4), (2,2), (3,2) \}$

4. a) $\{ (1,(0,a)), (1,(0,b)), (2,(0,a)), (2,(0,b)),$

$(3,(0,a)), (3,(0,b)) \}$

b) $\{ ((1,0),a), ((1,0),b), ((2,0),a), ((2,0),b),$

$((3,0),a), ((3,0),b) \}$

5. a) $\{ \phi, \{(0,a)\}, \{(1,a)\}, A \times B \}$

b) $\{ (\phi,\phi), (\phi,B), (\{0\},\phi), (\{0\},B), (\{1\},\phi), (\{1\},B),$

$((A,\phi), (A,B) \}$

6. a) 100 b) 2^{100} c) 2^{29}

7. The set of points inside the unit square

8. At least one is empty.

9. A and B are disjoint.

10. $A = B$

11. If $(x,y) \in A \times (B \cap C)$, then $x \in A$ and $y \in B \cap C$, so $y \in B$ and $y \in C$. Thus, $(x,y) \in (A \times B)$ and $(x,y) \in (A \times C)$, so $(x,y) \in (A \times B) \cap (A \times C)$. If $(x,y) \in (A \times B) \cap (A \times C)$, then $(x,y) \in A \times B$ and $(x,y) \in A \times C$. This means that $x \in A$ and $y \in B$ and $y \in C$. Thus, $y \in B \cap C$. So $(x,y) \in A \times (B \cap C)$.

12. Suppose $(x,y) \in (A \cap B) \times (C \cap D)$. Then $x \in A \cap B$ and $y \in C \cap D$. Since $x \in A$ and $y \in C$, $(x,y) \in A \times C$, and since $x \in B$ and $y \in D$, $(x,y) \in B \times D$. Therefore, $(x,y) \in (A \times C) \cap (B \times D)$. Suppose

$(x,y) \in (A \times C) \cap (B \times D)$. Then $(x,y) \in A \times C$ so $x \in A$ and $y \in C$. Also $(x,y) \in B \times D$ so $x \in B$ and $y \in D$. So $x \in A \cap B$ and $y \in C \cap D$. Therefore, $(x,y) \in (A \cap B) \times (C \cap D)$.

13. Suppose $(x,y) \in A \times C$. Then $x \in A$, so $x \in B$ since $A \subset B$. And $y \in C$, so $y \in D$ since $C \subset D$. Therefore, $(x,y) \in B \times D$ and so $A \times C \subset B \times D$.

14. Suppose $x \in A$ and $y \in C$ so that $(x,y) \in A \times C$. Since $A \times C \subset B \times D$, $(x,y) \in B \times D$. Thus, $x \in B$ and $y \in D$. So $A \subset B$ and $C \subset D$.

15. a) $I \times I \times I \times I \times R \times R$

    b) $R \times I \times R$

Section 2.5

1. $1 \longleftrightarrow a$, $2 \longleftrightarrow b$, $3 \longleftrightarrow c$, $4 \longleftrightarrow d$, $5 \longleftrightarrow e$
2. $f(a) = a + 1$
3. $f(n) = n^2$
4. a) $f(a) = 5a$ b) $f(a) = 5a + 15$
5. $f(b) = b/3$
6. a) yes b) no c) no d) no
7. For $x \in (0,1)$ define $f(x) = (b - a)x + a$
8. Assign to a set the bit string having 1's in the positions indicated by the numbers in the set.
9. For $n \in Z$, the function $f(n) = 2^n$ is a one-to-one correspondence between the set Z and the set of integral powers of 2.
10. The hint describes a one-to-one correspondence because there are only finitely many pairs having a given sum.
11. Let f(1) be the smallest element in the set, f(2) the next smallest, etc. This defines a function because for any a, f(a)

can be computed in a finite number of steps.

12. Let $.a_1a_2a_3...$ be the nonterminating decimal expansion of $x \in (0,1]$ and let $.b_1b_2b_3...$ be the nonterminating decimal expansion of $y \in (0,1]$. Define $f(x,y) = .a_1b_1a_2b_2a_3b_3....$

Section 2.6

1. a) Step 1: $n = 1$: $1 = 1^2$

Step 2: assume true for $n = k - 1$, that is

$$1 + 3 + 5 + ... + [2(k-1) - 1] = (k - 1)^2$$

then for $n = k$,

$$\begin{aligned} 1 + 3 + ... + [2(k-1) - 1] + (2k-1) &= (k - 1)^2 + (2k-1) \\ &= k^2 - 2k + 1 + 2k - 1 \\ &= k^2 \end{aligned}$$

b) Step 1: $n = 1$: $1 = 1(3-1)/2$

Step 2: assume true for $n = k-1$:

$$1 + 4 + 7 + ... + 3(k-1)-2 = (k-1)[3(k-1)-1]/2$$

then for $n = k$,

$$\begin{aligned} 1 + 4 + ... + 3(k-1)-2 + (3k-2) &= (k-1)[3(k-1)-1]/2 + (3k-2) \\ &= (k-1)(3k-4)/2 + (3k-2) \\ &= [(k-1)(3k-4) + 2(3k-2)]/2 \\ &= (3k^2 - 7k + 4 + 6k - 4)/2 \\ &= (3k^2 - k)/2 \\ &= k(3k - 1)/2 \end{aligned}$$

c) Step 1: $n = 1$: $1^2 = 1(1+1)[2(1) + 1]/6$

Step 2: assume true for $n = k-1$, that is,

$$1^2 + 2^2 + ... + (k-1)^2 = (k-1)[(k-1) + 1][2(k-1) + 1]/6$$

then for $n = k$,

$$1^2 + 2^2 + \ldots + (k-1)^2 + k^2 = (k-1)[(k-1)+1][2(k-1)+1]/6 + k^2$$
$$= (k-1)k(2k-1)/6 + k^2$$
$$= [(k-1)k(2k-1) + 6k^2]/6$$
$$= [(k^2-k)(2k-1) + 6k^2]/6$$
$$= (2k^3-3k^2-k^2+k+6k^2)/6$$
$$= (2k^3+3k^2+k)/6$$
$$= k(2k^2+3k+1)/6$$
$$= k(k+1)(2k+1)/6$$

2. a) Step 1: $n = 1$: $1^3 = [1(1+1)/2]^2$

Step 2: assume true for $n = k-1$, that is,

$$1^3 + 2^3 + \ldots + (k-1)^3 = [(k-1)((k-1)+1)/2]^2$$

then for $n = k$,

$$1^3 + 2^3 + \ldots + (k-1)^3 + k^3 = [(k-1)((k-1)+1)/2]^2 + k^3$$
$$= [(k-1)k/2]^2 + k^3$$
$$= [(k^2 - k)/2]^2 + k^3$$
$$= (k^2 - k)^2/4 + k^3$$
$$= [(k^2 - k)^2 + 4k^3]/4$$
$$= (k^4 - 2k^3 + k^2 + 4k^3)/4$$
$$= (k^4 + 2k^3 + k^2)/4$$
$$= k^2(k^2 + 2k + 1)/4$$
$$= k^2(k + 1)^2/4$$
$$= [k(k+1)/2]^2$$

b) Step 1: $n = 1$: $1/1(2) = 1/(1 + 1)$

Step 2: assume true for $n = k-1$, that is,

$$1/1(2) + 1/2(3) + \ldots + 1/(k-1)k = (k-1)/k$$

then for $n = k$,

$1/1(2) + 1/2(3) + \ldots + 1/(k-1)k + 1/k(k+1) = (k-1)/k + 1/k(k+1)$

$= [(k-1)(k+1) + 1]/k(k+1)$

$= [(k^2 - 1) + 1]/k(k+1)$

$= k^2/k(k+1)$

$= k/(k+1)$

c) Step 1: $n = 1$: $2^1 = 2 = 2^{1+1} - 2$

Step 2: assume true for $n = k-1$:

$2 + 4 + \ldots + 2^{k-1} = 2^k - 2$

then for $n = k$,

$2 + 4 + \ldots + 2^{k-1} + 2^k = 2^k - 2 + 2^k$

$= 2(2^k) - 2$

$= 2^{k+1} - 2$

3. Step 1: $n = 1$: $2^1 = 2 > 1$

Step 2: assume true for $n = k-1$: $2^{k-1} > k-1$

then for $n = k$:

$2^k = 2(2^{k-1}) = 2^{k-1} + 2^{k-1}$

$> (k-1) + 2^{k-1}$ (by inductive hypotheses)

$\geq (k-1) + 1$ (since $2^{k-1} \geq 1$)

$= k$

4. Step 1: $n = 5$: $2^5 = 32 > 5^2$

Step 2: assume true for $n = k-1$:

$2^{k-1} > (k-1)^2$

then for $n = k$, $2^k = 2(2^{k-1})$

$> 2(k-1)^2 = 2(k^2 - 2k + 1)$

$= 2k^2 - 4k + 2$

$= k^2 + (k^2 - 4k + 2)$

$> k^2 + (k^2 - 4k) = k^2 + k(k - 4)$

$> k^2$ since $k \geq 5$

5. Step 1: $n = 1$: $a^1 < b^1$

Step 2: assume true for $n = k-1$: $a^{k-1} < b^{k-1}$

then for $n = k$, $a^k = a(a^{k-1}) < b(b^{k-1}) = b^k$

6. Step 1: $n = 1$: $1 + 2 \leq 3^1$

Step 2: assume true for $n = k-1$:

$1 + 2(k-1) \leq 3^{k-1}$

then

$$1 + 2k = 3 + 2k - 2 = 3 + 2(k-1) = 2 + 1 + 2(k-1)$$

$$\leq 2 + 3^{k-1} \leq 3^{k-1} + 3^{k-1} + 3^{k-1} = 3^k$$

7. Step 1: $n = 2$:

$1/\sqrt{1} + 1/\sqrt{2} = 1 + 0.707... > 1.414... = \sqrt{2}$

Step 2: assume true for $n = k-1$:

$1/\sqrt{1} + 1/\sqrt{2} + ... + 1/\sqrt{(k-1)} > \sqrt{(k-1)}$

then for $n = k$,

$1/\sqrt{1} + 1/\sqrt{2} + ... + 1/\sqrt{(k-1)} + 1/\sqrt{k} > \sqrt{(k-1)} + 1/\sqrt{k}$

Thus, it suffices to show that $\sqrt{(k-1)} + 1/\sqrt{k} > \sqrt{k}$. But for $k \geq 2$,

$$k(k-1) > (k-1)^2$$

$$\sqrt{[k(k - 1)]} > k - 1$$

$$\sqrt{[k(k - 1)]} + 1 > k$$

and the result follows upon dividing by $\sqrt{k}$.

8. Step 1: $n = 1$: After 1 year, the amount earned is the original investment P, plus the interest after 1 year, that is, $P + Pr = P(1 + r) = P(1 + r)^1$.

Step 2: assume true for $n = k-1$ years: amount earned is

$$P(1 + r)^{k-1}$$

then after k years, the amount earned is the amount earned after k-1 years, plus the interest earned in the k-th year, that is,

$$P(1 + r)^{k-1} + r[P(1 + r)^{k-1}] = P(1 + r)^{k-1}(1 + r)$$
$$= P(1 + r)^{k}$$

9. a) Step 1: $n = 1$: $(A_1)' = A_1'$

Step 2: assume true for $n = k-1$:

$$(A_1 \cap A_2 \cap \ldots \cap A_{k-1})' = A_1' \cup A_2' \cup \ldots \cup A_{k-1}'$$

then for $n = k$,

$$(A_1 \cap A_2 \cap \ldots \cap A_{k-1} \cap A_k)' = [(A_1 \cap A_2 \cap \ldots \cap A_{k-1}) \cap A_k)]'$$
$$= (A_1 \cap A_2 \cap \ldots \cap A_{k-1} \cap A_k)' \cup A_k'$$
$$= (A_1' \cup A_2' \cup \ldots \cup A_{k-1}') \cup A_k$$
$$= A_1' \cup \ldots \cup A_k'$$

b) interchange the $\cup$ and $\cap$ symbols in part a)

10. Step 1: $n = 1$: $A_1 \cup B = A_1 \cup B$

Step 2: assume true for $n = k-1$:

$$(A_1 \cap \ldots \cap A_{k-1}) \cup B = (A_1 \cup B) \cap \ldots \cap (A_{k-1} \cup B)$$

then for $n = k$,

$$(A_1 \cap \ldots \cap A_{k-1} \cap A_k) \cup B = [(A_1 \cap \ldots \cap A_{k-1}) \cap A_k] \cup B$$
$$= [(A_1 \cap \ldots \cap A_{k-1} \cap A_k) \cup B] \cap (A_k \cup B)$$
$$= (A_1 \cup B) \cap \ldots \cap (A_{k-1} \cup B) \cap (A_k \cup B)$$

11. The sum is $n + 1$. Step 1: for $n = 0$, the equation reads $1 = 1$. Step 2:

$$\sum_{i=0}^{k} 1^i = \sum_{i=0}^{k-1} 1^i + 1^k = (k - 1) + 1 = k$$

12. Step 1: if $m = 1$, $H_{2^1} \geq 1/2$ is true.

Step 2: $H_{2^k} = H_{2^{(k-1)}} + 1/(2^{k-1} + 1) + \ldots + 1/2^k$

By the induction hypothesis, $H_{2^{(k-1)}} \geq (k-1)/2$, and the remaining 2^{k-1} terms are each at least $1/2^k$.

13. If n = 2, $X_1 \cap X_2$ may be empty and z does not exist.

14. You can't prove $x^1 = 1$ because if you substitute k = 0 in the equation, you see that you need to assume that $x^1 = 1$ in order to prove that $x^1 = 1$.

15. Let S' = S ∪ { 1, 2, ..., n_0 }. Then S' satisfies the condition of the weak form of mathematical induction, so S' = N. Then S is N less the numbers less than n_0.

16. a) If T $\neq \phi$, then by the Well-Ordering Principle, T has a least element, call it x. Then x − 1 $\notin$ T, so x − 1 ϵ S. The condition on S then states that x ϵ S, contradicting x ϵ T.

    b) Step 1: 1 ϵ S, for if 1 ϵ T, then 1 would be the least element of T. Step 2: Let x ϵ N, x > 1, and suppose that all natural numbers less then x are in S. If s were in T, then x would be the least element of T, which is assumed not to exist. Therefore, x ϵ S. Consequently, the principle of induction applies.

Section 2.7

1. A: 11000100; B: 00111110; C: 00101011; X: 11111111
2. a) 11111110 b) 00000000 c) 00111010 d) 11010100
3. a) 00000101 b) 4 and 5 c) 1, 3, and 6

   d) 1, 2, 4, and 6 e) 3 and 4
4. a) None b) None c) 5

Chapter Review

1. { (1,0), (2,0), (3,0), (4,0), (2,1), (3,1), (4,1), (3,2), (4,2), (4,3) }
2. { ϕ, {1}, {2}, {3}, {1,2}, {1,3}, {2,3}, {1,2,3} }
3. f(1) = a, f(2) = b, etc. in order. There are many others.

4. $f(n) = 4n$

5. $f(x) = x$

6. a) $[-5,3)$ b) $(-2,2)$ c) $(1,\infty)$

7. a) $(-1,3)$ b) $(0,1]$ c) $(-2,5]$

d) $(-\infty,0] \cup [1,2)$ e) $[3,5]$

8. a) $(1,\infty)$ b) $(-\infty,-1] \cup [1,\infty)$

c) $(-\infty,2) \cup (5,\infty)$ d) $(-\infty,-1]$

9. If $x \in A - (B \cap C)$, then $x \in A$ and x is not in both B and C. If x is not in B, then $x \in A - B$, and if x in not in C, then $x \in A - C$. This shows that $A - (B \cup C) \subset (A - B) \cup (A - C)$. Now suppose $x \in (A - B) \cup (A - C)$. Then either $x \in A - B$ or $x \in A - C$. If $x \in A - C$, then $x \in A - (B \cap C)$, and the other case is similar.

10. a) Step 1: if $n = 1$, $2 = 1^2 + 1$.

Step 2: $2 + 4 + \ldots + 2k = (k-1)^2 + (k-1) + 2k$

$= k^2 - 2k + 1 + k - 1 + 2k = k^2 + k$

b) Step 1: if $n = 1$, $1 + 1/2 = 2 - 1/2^1$

Step 2: $1 + 1/2 + \ldots + 1/2^{k-1} + 1/2^k$

$= (2 - 1/2^{k-1}) + 1/2^k$

$= 2 - 2/2^k + 1/2^k = 2 - 1/2^k$

c) Step 1: If $n = 4$, $4! = 2^4$ and $24 > 16$.

Step 2: If $k > 4$, $k! = k \times (k-1)! > 2 \times 2^{k-1} = 2^k$

11. a) Step 1: If $n = 1$, $1 - 1/2 = 1/(1 + 1)$

Step 2: If $k > 1$,

$(1 - 1/2)(1 - 1/3) \ldots [1 - 1/(k+1)]$

$= (1 - 1/2)(1 - 1/3) \ldots (1 - 1/k)[1 - 1/(k+1)]$

$= (1/k)(k/(k + 1)) = 1/(k + 1)$

b) Step 1: If $n = 1$, $1 = (3^1 - 1)/2$

Step 2: $1 + 3 + \ldots + 3^{k-1}$

$= 1 + 3 + \ldots + 3^{k-2} + 3^{k-1}$

$= (3^{k-1} - 1)/2 + 3^{k-1}$

$= [3^{k-1} - 1 + 2(3^{k-1})]/2$

$= [3(3^{k-1}) - 1]/2 = (3^k - 1)/2$

c) Step 1: If $n = 1$, $2(1) \leq 2^1$

Step 2: If $k > 1$, $2k = 2(k - 1) + 2 \leq 2^{k-1} + 2$

$\leq 2^{k-1} + 2^{k-1} = 2^k$

12. A: 100110 B: 010011 C: 001000

13. a) 000010 b) 100100 c) 100100

d) 010001 e) 111101 f) 100100

g) 110111

Chapter 3

Section 3.1

1. a) x b) x c) z + x d) x

2. a) 9 b) 144

3. { (1,u), (1,v) }

4.

	domain	image
a)	{ a,b,u,n,m }	{ n,d,g,s }
b)	{ 1,2,3,4 }	{ 1,√2,√3,2 }

5. No – the range can be any set containing the image.

6. Image is { -1,0,1 }.

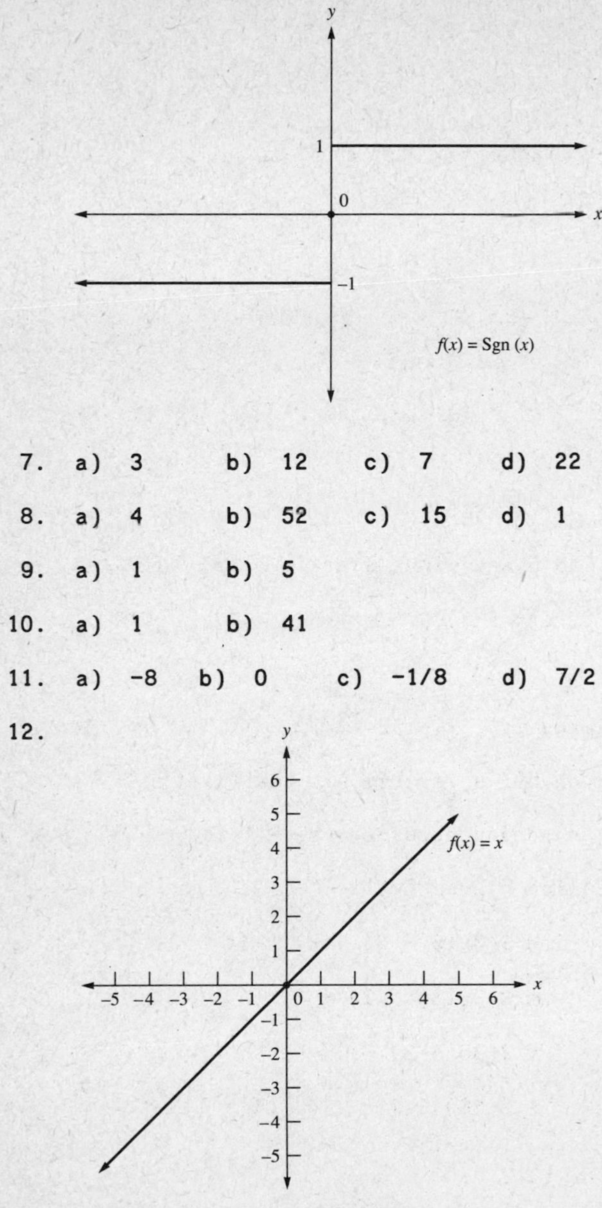

7. a) 3 b) 12 c) 7 d) 22

8. a) 4 b) 52 c) 15 d) 1

9. a) 1 b) 5

10. a) 1 b) 41

11. a) −8 b) 0 c) −1/8 d) 7/2

12.

13. Image is set of non-negative real numbers.

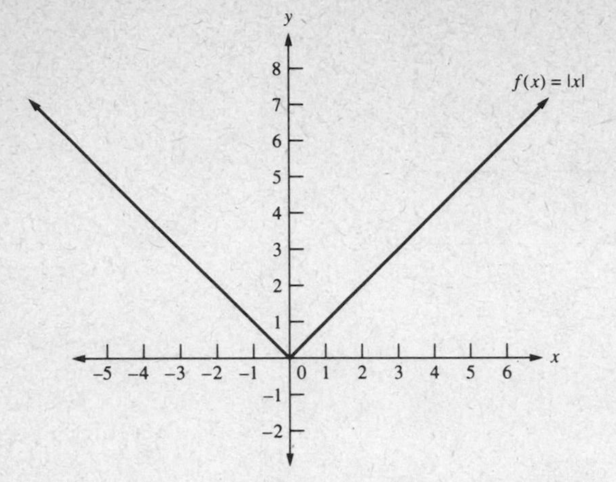

14. It contains the pairs (x,y_1) and (x,y_2).

15. a) 5 b) 0 c) If x = 5,

then left side is equal to 5 and right side is equal to 6.

16. a) n^3 b) 2^n c) 2^{n-1} d) $(-1)^n$

17. a) $(-1)^{n-1}$ b) 1/n c) $(1/2)^n$ d) $(1/10)^n$

18. a) In both cases the image is { 1, 1/2, 1/3, 1/4, ... }.

b) The n-th term is given by: s_n = 1/n for the first sequence, and for the second sequence, s_n = 1 for n odd, and 2/(n + 2) for n even.

19. a) $3(3(5(3) - 3) + 2) - 1 = 3(3(15 - 3) + 2) - 1$

$= 3(3(12) + 2) - 1$

$= 3(36 + 2) - 1$

$= 3(38) - 1 = 114 - 1 = 113$

b) 2 compared to 6

20. { (a,a), (b,a) } { (a,a), (b,b) }

{ (a,b), (b,b) } { (a,b), (b,a) }

21. 8 from A to B, 9 from B to A

22. If $b \in f[X \cup Y]$, then $b = f(a)$ where $a \in X \cup Y$. So either $a \in X$ or $a \in Y$. If $a \in X$, then $f(a) = b \in f[X] \subset f[X] \cup f[Y]$.

Similarly if $a \in Y$. Conversely, if $b \in f[X] \cup f[Y]$, then either $b \in f[X]$ or $b \in f[Y]$. If $b \in f[X]$, then $b = f(a)$ for some $a \in X \subset X \cup Y$. So $b \in f[X \cup Y]$. Similarly if $b \in f[Y]$.

23. Define $f: \{ 1, 2 \} \to \{ 1 \}$ by $f(1) = f(2) = 1$. Let $X = \{ 1 \}$ and $Y = \{ 2 \}$. Then $X \cap Y = \phi$ and $f[X \cap Y] = \phi$, but $f[X] \cap f[Y] = \{ 1 \}$.

24. No - Grover Cleveland served two nonconsecutive terms and so he had two different successors.

Section 3.2

1. a) onto b) both c) both d) one-to-one
2. a) neither b) both
3. a) neither b) one-to-one c) one-to-one
4. a) both b) neither
   c) neither d) one-to-one
5. Not one-to-one since $0! = 1! = 1$. Not onto since the image is not equal to N.
6. No, since $s_1 = s_2 = 1$. No, since the image is not equal to N.
7. no, no
8. Onto but not one-to-one
9. no, no
10. $f^{-1} = \{ (x,a), (y,b), (v,c), (w,d) \}$
11. No, since f is not one-to-one.
12. No, since f is not onto.
13. $f^{-1}(x) = (x + 1)/3$
14. $f(g(x) = f(\sqrt[3]{x}) = (\sqrt[3]{x})^3 = x$ and
    $g(f(x) = g(x^3) = \sqrt[3]{(x^3)} = x$

15. $f \circ g = \{ (a,e), (b,b), (c,d), (d,b), (e,b) \}$

$g \circ f = \{ (1,1), (2,4), (3,1), (4,1) \}$

16. a) $(x + 1)^2$ b) $x^2 + 1$

17. a) $(2n + 5)^2 + 1$ b) $(n^2 + 1)^2 + 1$

c) $2(n^2 + 1) + 5$ d) $2(2n + 5) + 5$

18. The functions g^{-1} and f^{-1} exist since both f and g are one-to-one and onto. If $a \in A$, then

$$[(f^{-1} \circ g^{-1}) \circ (g \circ f)](a) = f^{-1}(g^{-1}(g(f(a))))$$
$$= f^{-1}(f(a)) = a$$

and similarly, if $b \in b$,

$$[(g \circ f) \circ (f^{-1} \circ g^{-1})](b) = g(f(f^{-1}(g^{-1}(b))))$$
$$= g(g^{-1}(b)) = b$$

Now apply Theorem 3.2.

19. $(f + g)(x) = x^2 + 1 + 1 - x = x^2 - x + 2$

$(f - g)(x) = x^2 + 1 - (1 - x) = x^2 + x$

$(fg)(x) = (x^2 + 1)(1 - x) = -x^3 + x^2 - 1 + 1$

20. Suppose $f(a) = f(b)$. Then $a^3 + 1 = b^3 + 1$, so that $a^3 = b^3$ and $a = b$.

21. Suppose that $(g \circ f)(x) = (g \circ f)(y)$. That is, $g(f(x)) = g(f(y))$. Since g is one-to-one, $f(x) = f(y)$, and since f is one-to-one, $x = y$.

22. Suppose $x \in C$. Since g is onto, $x = g(y)$ for some $y \in B$. Since f is onto, $y = f(z)$ for some $z \in A$. So $x = g(f(z))$.

23. Suppose f is one-to-one. If f is not onto, then there is an $x \in B$ such that $x \neq f(a)$ for any $a \in A$. So there are are at most n-1 elements in the image of f. Since there are n elements in A, at least two elements in A must have the same image in B (by the

Pigeonhole principle). This is impossible because f is one-to-one. Conversely, suppose f is onto and f is not one-to-one. Then there are distinct elements x and y in A such that $f(x) = f(y)$. So the image of f contains at most $n-1$ elements. This is impossible since f is onto.

24. yes, yes

25. a) $\{ 1 \}$ b) $\{ 2,3,4 \}$ c) ϕ d) X

26. Let $x \in f^{-1}[B']$. Then $f(x) \in B'$. To show that $x \in (f^{-1}[B])'$, we must show that $x \notin f^{-1}[B]$. But if $x \in f^{-1}[B]$, then we would also have $f(x) \in B$, contradicting $f(x) \in B'$. Conversely, suppose $x \in (f^{-1}[B])'$. Then $x \notin f^{-1}[B]$. Therefore $f(x) \notin B$. Consequently, $f(x) \in B'$ and $x \in f^{-1}[B']$.

27. Let $X = \{ 1, 2 \}$, $Y = N$, $f(1) = f(2) = 1$, $A = \{ 1 \}$. Then $f[A'] = f[\{ 2 \}] = \{ 1 \}$ but $(f[A])' = \{ 1 \}' = N - \{ 1 \}$.

28. a)

n	1	2	3	4	5	6	7	8
f(n)	1	2	1/2	3	1/3	3/2	2/3	4

n	9	10	11	12	13	14	15
f(n)	1/4	4/3	3/4	5/2	2/5	5/3	3/5

b) "All of the numbers f(1) are different" is true since there is only one number. Assume that all of the numbers f(1) through $f(n - 1)$ are different; we must show that f(n) is different from all of f(1), ..., $f(n - 1)$. Suppose that $f(n) = f(k)$ where $k < n$. If n is odd, then it follows from the third part of the definition of f that $f(k - 1) = f(n - 1)$, contradicting the induction hypothesis. If n is even, then so is k, because $f(x) > 1$ only for even values of x. It then follows from the second part of the definition of f that $f(k/2) = f(n/2)$, also contradicting the induction hypothesis.

c) "All rational numbers x with $s(x) \le 2$ are in the image of f" is true, since the only rational number number x with $s(x) \le 2$ is 1. Assume that all rational numbers x with $s(x) \le n - 1$ are in the image of f, and let y be a rational number with $s(y) = n$. Let $y = a/b$ be the lowest terms representation of y. If $y > 1$, then $a > b$; set $z = y - 1 = (a - b)/b$. Then $s(z) = a - b + b < s(x)$. By the induction hypothesis, z is in the image of f; say, $z = f(k)$. Then $f(2k) = z + 1 = y$. If, on the other hand, $y < 1$, a similar argument can be applied to show that 1/y is in the image of f. If $f(k) = 1/y$, then $f(k + 1) = y$.

Section 3.3

1. $2^9 = 512$ relations; 27 functions

2. a) { (1,2), (2,1), (1,3), (3,3), (3,2), (4,1), (4,2) }

   b) { (1,4), (2,1), (2,4), (4,1) }

   c) { (1,2), (2,2), (2,3), (3,1), (3,4) }

3.

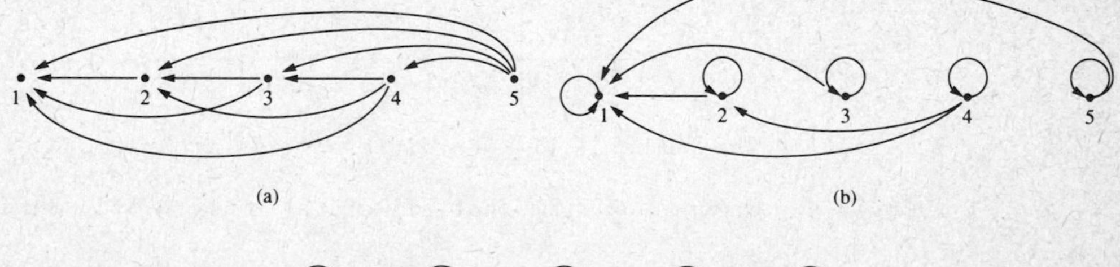

(a) (b)

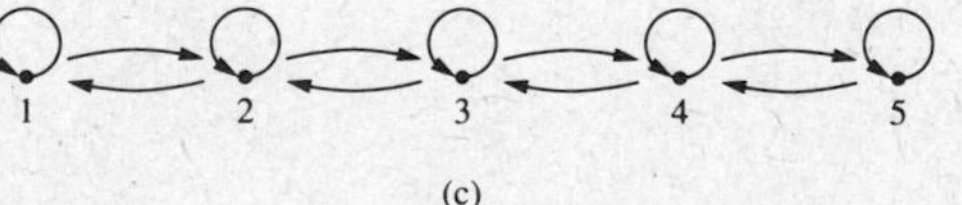

(c)

4. a) symmetric and transitive

   b) reflexive and symmetric

   c) reflexive and transitive

5. a) symmetric

b) reflexive, symmetric, and transitive

c) symmetric

6. a) transitive

b) symmetric

c) symmetric and transitive

7.

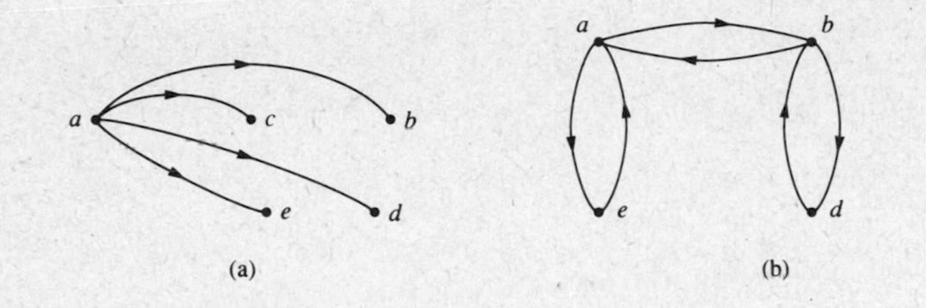

(a) (b)

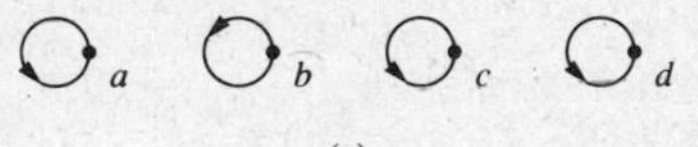

(c)

8. none, none, none

9. $(x,y,z) \in R \times R \times R$ if $x + y + z < 1$

10. reflexive, symmetric, and transitive

11. reflexive, symmetric, and transitive

12. reflexive and transitive

13. Given a, there does not necessarily exist any b for which a R b. For instance, let A = { 1,2,3 } and R = { (1,1), (1,2), (2,1) }; nothing is related to 3.

14. relation b

15. relations a and b

16. The relation of Exercise 6 b)

17. The relation of Exercise 6 c)

18. relation c

19. relation a

20. The empty relation

21. If R is asymmetric and if $(a,a) \in R$, then $(a,a) \notin R$, a contradiction. Therefore, $(a,a) \notin R$.

22. No, see Exercise 2 b).

Section 3.4

1.

If	then
a R a and a R a	a R a
a R a and a R b	a R b
a R b and b R a	a R a
a R b and b R b	a R b
b R a and a R a	b R a
b R a and a R b	b R b
b R b and b R a	b R a
b R b and b R b	b R b
c R c and c R c	c R c
c R c and c R d	c R d
c R d and d R c	c R c
c R d and d R d	c R d
d R c and c R d	d R d
d R c and c R c	d R c
d R d and d R c	d R c
d R d and d R d	d R d
e R e and e R e	e R e

2. No, it is not possible to prove transitivity since $(x,0) \in Z \times Z$.

3. Reflexive: $(x,y)\ S\ (x,y)$ is true since $x + y = y + x$ by the commutative law.

Symmetric: If $(x,y)\ S\ (z,w)$, then $x + w = y + z$ and $y + z = x + w$ since equality is symmetric, and $z + y = w + x$ so $(z,w)\ S\ (x,y)$.

Transitive: Suppose $(x,y)\ S\ (z,w)$ and $(z,w)\ S\ (u,v)$. Then $x - y = z - w$ and $z - w = u - v$, so that $x - y = u - v$, and $(x,y)\ S\ (u,v)$.

4. Reflexive: $x - x = 0 = 0m$ so $x \equiv x \pmod{m}$

   Symmetric: If $x \equiv y \pmod{m}$, then $x - y = mk$ and $y - x = -(x - y) = -mk = m(-k) = mh$ for some integer h. So $y \equiv x \pmod{m}$.

   Transitive: Suppose $x \equiv y \pmod{m}$ and $y \equiv z \pmod{m}$. Then $x - y = mk$ and $y - z = mh$ so that $x - z = x - y + y - z = mk + mh = m(k + h) = mt$ for some integer t.

5.

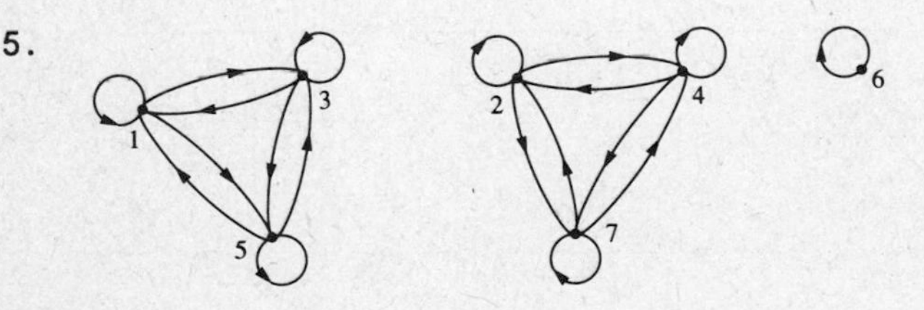

6. Reflexive: $(x,y)\ \#\ (x,y)$ since $xy = yx$

   Symmetric: If $(x,y)\ \#\ (z,w)$, then $xw = yz$ so $zy = wx$ which means that $(z,w)\ \#\ (x,y)$.

   Transitive: If $(x,y)\ \#\ (z,w)$ and $(z,w)\ \#\ (u,v)$, then $xw = yz$ and $zv = wu$. Therefore, $xwv = yzv = ywu$. Since $w \neq 0$, w can be canceled yielding $xv = yu$, that is, $(x,y)\ \#\ (u,v)$. The equivalence classes are the sets of pairs (x,y) for which the ratios x/y are equal. Geometrically, the equivalence classes are the lines in the plane that pass through the origin, with the origin omitted.

7. a) Sets of form { a, −a } where $a \in R$

b) Half-open intervals [n, n + 1) where $n \in N$

c) Half-open intervals (n, n + 1] where $n \in N$

d) Lines of slope 2/3

e) If $x^2 + y^2 = b$, then the level set is the circle centered at (0, 0) with radius $\sqrt{b}$.

8. The subsets of X consisting of single elements.

9.

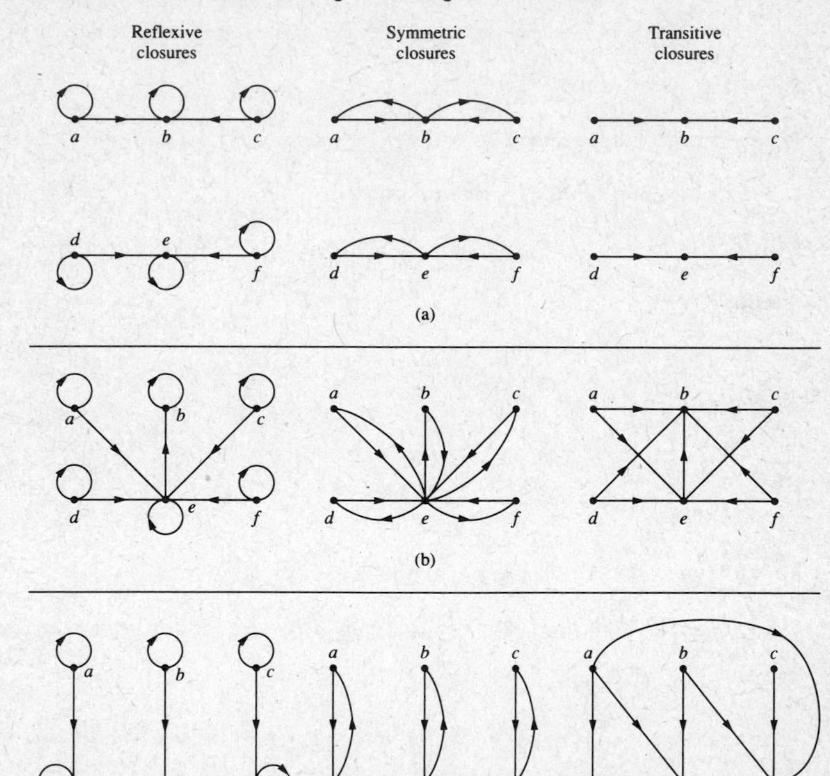

10.

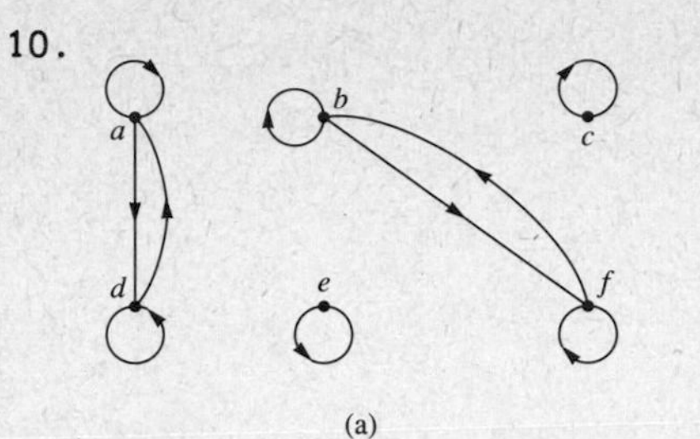

(a)

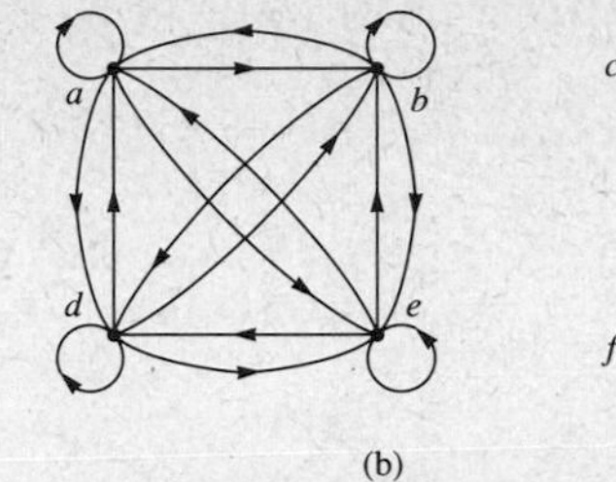

(b)

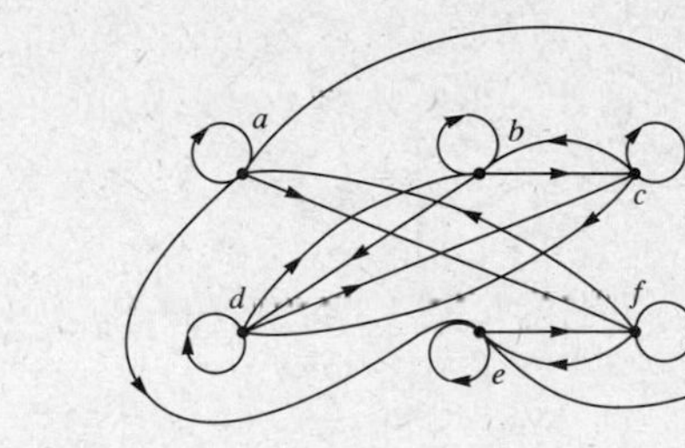

(d)

a b c d e f

(c)

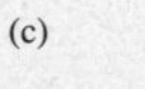

11. "is a descendent of"

12. Add the pairs (a,a), (b,b), and (c,c)

13. Add the pairs (b,a), (b,c), (c,a)

14. R is transitive as defined.

15. a ≡ b (mod 0) means a = b so each equivalence class is a set consisting of a single integer.

16. If a is a bit string, define R to be: a R a if a = a or a is the one's complement of a. The equivalence classes contain two elements: a word and its one's complement.

Section 3.5

1.

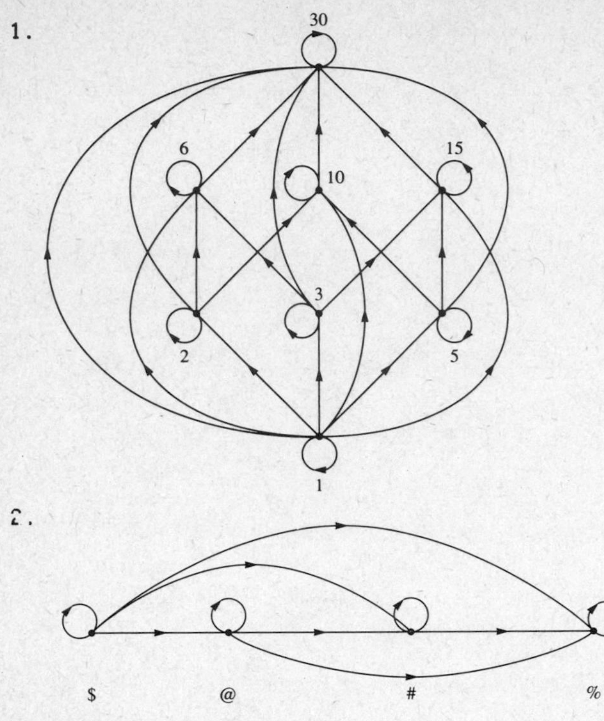

3. a, b, d

4. All are partial orders. None are total orders.

5. Part c is a partial order

6. Sets with one element

7. Since x R y is always false, there are no pairs (x,y) and (y,x) with x $\neq$ y.

8. Suppose R is a relation and S is a subset of R. Then if (x,y) and (y,x) are elements of S, (x,y) and (y,x) are elements of R and so x = y.

9. If R is a relation that is not antisymmetric, and if R $\subset$ S, then S is not antisymmetric. (For if a $\neq$ b, a R b, and b R a, then also a S b and b S a.) Therefore, if R is not antisymmetric, antisymmetry cannot be restored by adding more ordered pairs to

it.

10. Suppose that the relation R on the set X is not antisymmetric. Then there exist a and b in X such that a R b, b R a, and $a \neq b$. Therefore, R is not asymmetric.

11. $\geq$

12. The empty relation.

13. Suppose that the relation R on the set X is not asymmetric. Then there exist $a \in X$ and $b \in X$ such that a R b and b R a. By transitivity, a R a, contradicting irreflexivity.

Section 3.6

(In the following answers, * indicates a key field.)

1. R1: { *Employee SSN, Employee Name, Skill }

   R2: { *Customer Name, Customer Address }

   R3: { *Contract number, Customer Name }

   R4: { *Job no., contract number }

   R5: { *Employee SSN, *Week, *Job Number, Hours worked }

2. R1: { *Rocket sn, widget sn, transmogrifier sn }

   R2: { *Widget sn, Manufacturer, Contract number, Test facility, Test Date }

   R3: { *Transmogrifier sn, Manufacturer, Contract number, Test facility, Test Date }

   R4: { *Manufacturer, Manufacturer address }

   R5: { *Test facility, Test facility address }

3. R1: { *Item number, Location where found, Date found, Culture, Finder, Organization }

   R2: { *Culture, Period }

   R3: { *Finder, Finder's current address }

R4: { *Organzation, Organization's current address }

Chapter Review

1. { (-1,-2), (0,-1), (1/3,-26/27), (2,7) }

2. a) 2 b) 9

3. Domain is { 1,2,3,5 }, image is { 1,4,9,25 }

4. Image is { 1, 4, 9, 16, 25, ... }, $f(n) = n^2$

5. { (1,a), (2,b), (3,c) } , no

6. a) f(x) = c for each $x \in A$

   b) f(1) = a, and so on in order

   c) No, by the result of Exercise 27, Section 3.2

7. a) neither b) onto

8. Let f(a) = a + 1

9. b) no c) no

10. 9, 6, 8, 0

11. a) { (u,a), (w,b), (z,c), (x,d) }

    b) { (1,-1), (0,0), (-1,1) }

12. f(g(x)) = 5[(x-2)/5] + 2 = (x-2) + 2 = x

    g(f(x)) = [(5x+2) - 2]/5 = 5x/5 = x

13. No; f is not onto.

14. If f(a) = f(b), then 2a - 9 = 2b - 9, so 2a = 2b and a = b.

15. { (1,1), (1,2) }

16. Let A = { 1, 2, 3 }

    a) { (1,2), (2,3) }

    b) { (1,1), (2,2), (3,3), (1,2), (2,3) }

    c) { (1,2), (2,1) }

    d) { (1,2) }

17. Let A = { 1, 2, 3 }

a) { (1,1), (2,2), (3,3), (1,2), (2,1), (2,3), (3,2) }

b) { (1,1), (2,2), (3,3), (1,2) }

c) { (1,1), (1,2), (2,1) }

d) { (1,1), (2,2), (3,3) }

18. 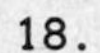

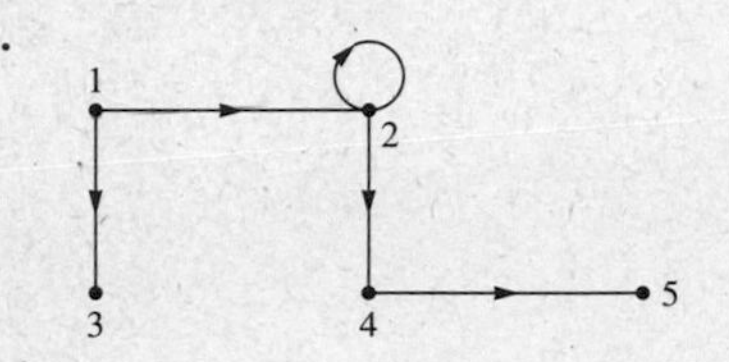

19. Not reflexive since 0 is not prime; symmetric; not transitive (12 R 7 and 7 R 4 but 12 R 4 is false.)

20. Reflexive: yes since 0 = 0

Symmetric: yes since c − a = −(a − c) = −(b − d) = d − b

Transitive: yes since a − e = a − c + c − e = a − c + d − f

= b − d + d − f = b − f

21.

a b

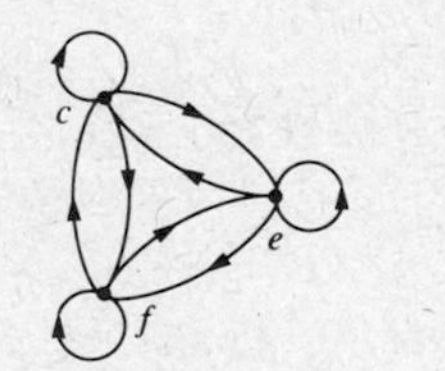

d

22. Add the pair (a,c)

23. For a, b ∈ B, define R to be: a R b if a = b or a is the two's complement of b. The equivalence classes are { 00000000 }, { 10000000 }, and doubletons consisting of the representations of n and −n for n = 1, ..., 127.

24.

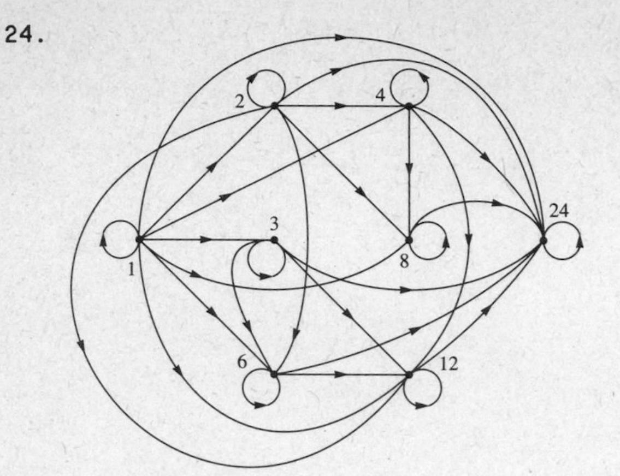

25.

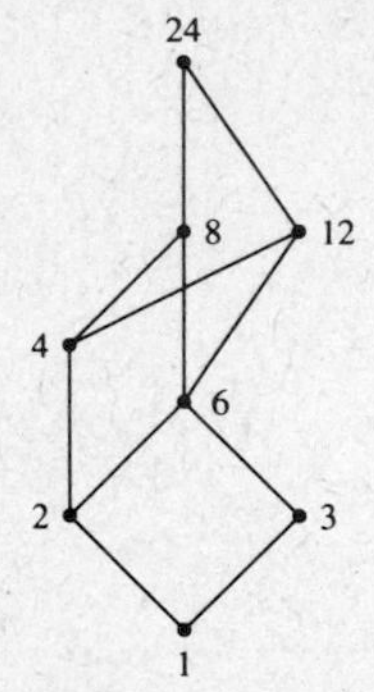

26. a) Z with the divisibility relation

b) R with the relation $\leq$

27. For X non-empty, R is symmetric, transitive, antisymmetric, asymmetric, and irreflexive. For X empty, R has all six properties.

28. (In this answer, * indicates a key field)

{ *Student name, Pick-up point }

{ *Pick-up point, Route number }

{ *Route number, School }

{ *Bus number, Route number }

29. Note that if a is of odd ancestry, then its first-order ancester is of even ancestry. Let E_x, O_x, I_x consist of the elements of X

having even, odd, and infinite ancestry respectively; similarly define E_Y, O_Y, I_Y. Define h: X $\longrightarrow$ Y by h(x) = f(x) if x is of even or infinite ancestry, and h(x) = the first-order ancestor of x if x is of odd ancestry. Then h maps I_X to I_Y, E_X to O_Y, and O_X to E_Y.

30. Refer to Exercise 12, Section 1.5, for a one-to-one function from (0,1] x (0,1] to (0,1], and use the result of Exercise 29.

Chapter 4

Section 4.1

1. a, c, e

2. a) The set of integers is not finite.

   b) F.D.Roosevelt was not elected president in 1944.

   c) It is not true that 6 is not a prime number.

3. a) 5 is prime and 1/3 is rational.

   b) Nixon was elected president in 1968 and 1972 and Nixon did not complete two terms as president.

4. π is a natural number or Euclid is the author of Proof.

5. a) If Euclid was born in Sardinia, then Euclid was not six feet tall.

   b) Euclid was born in Sardinia if and only if Euclid was six feet tall.

   c) It is not true that Euclid was both not born in Sardinia and was six feet tall.

   d) Euclid was not born in Sardinia nor was Euclid six feet tall.

6. a) $p \Longrightarrow q$ b) $p \Longrightarrow q$ c) $p \wedge q$

7. a) $q \Longrightarrow p$ b) $\neg(q \wedge \neg p)$; or, q NAND $\neg p$

   c) $\neg q \Longrightarrow p$

8. a) Converse: If $f \circ g$ is one-to-one, then f and g are one-to-one. Contrapositive: If $f \circ g$ is not one-to-one, then f and g are not one-to-one.

   b) Converse: If a polygon is a parallelogram, then it is a square. Contrapositive: If a polygon is not a parallelogram, then it is not a square.

9.

p	q	$p \veebar q$
T	T	F
T	F	T
F	T	T
F	F	F

10.

p	q	$p \Leftarrow q$	$p \not\Leftarrow q$	$p \not\Rightarrow q$
T	T	T	F	F
T	F	T	F	T
F	T	F	T	F
F	F	T	F	F

11. a) $q \Rightarrow p$ b) $\neg(p \Rightarrow q)$ c) $\neg(q \Rightarrow p)$

12. AND: 01000101; OR: 11011111; XOR: 10011010; NOT: 10110010

13. 256

14.

and	T	U	F
T	T	U	F
U	U	U	F
F	F	F	F

or	T	U	F
T	T	T	T
U	T	U	U
F	T	U	F

not	
T	F
U	U
F	T

$\Rightarrow$	T	U	F
T	T	U	F
U	T	U	U
F	T	T	T

Section 4.2

1.

p	q	$\neg p \wedge q$	$p \vee \neg q$	$\neg p \Rightarrow q$	$\neg(p \Rightarrow q)$
T	T	F	T	T	F
T	F	F	T	T	T
F	T	T	F	T	F
F	F	F	T	F	F

2.

p	q	$p \veebar \neg q$	$\neg(p \veebar q)$	$\neg p \veebar q$	$\neg p \Rightarrow (p \Rightarrow q)$
T	T	T	T	T	T
T	F	F	F	F	T
F	T	F	F	F	T
F	F	T	T	T	T

3. a)

p	$p \Rightarrow p$
T	T
F	T

b)

p	q	$q \Rightarrow p$	$p \Rightarrow (q \Rightarrow p)$
T	T	T	T
T	F	T	T
F	T	F	T
F	F	T	T

c)

p	q	$p \Rightarrow q$	$\neg p$	$\neg p \vee q$	$(p \Rightarrow q) \Leftrightarrow (\neg p \vee q)$
T	T	T	F	T	T
T	F	F	F	F	T
F	T	T	T	T	T
F	F	T	T	T	T

d)

p	q	r	$p \wedge q$	$q \wedge r$	$(p \wedge q) \wedge r$	$p \wedge (q \wedge r)$	$(p \wedge q) \wedge r \Leftrightarrow p \wedge (q \wedge r)$
T	T	T	T	T	T	T	T
T	T	F	T	F	F	F	T
T	F	T	F	F	F	F	T
T	F	F	F	F	F	F	T
F	T	T	F	T	F	F	T
F	T	F	F	F	F	F	T
F	F	T	F	F	F	F	T
F	F	F	F	F	F	F	T

4. a)

p	q	$p \wedge q$	$\neg p \vee \neg q$	$\neg(\neg p \vee \neg q)$	$\neg(\neg p \vee \neg q)$
T	T	T	F	T	T
T	F	F	T	F	T
F	T	F	T	F	T
F	F	F	T	F	T

b)

p	q	$p\ q$	p NAND q	$p \wedge q \Leftrightarrow (p$ NAND $q)$ NAND $(p$ NAND $q)$
T	T	T	F	T
T	F	F	T	T
F	T	F	T	T
F	F	F	T	T

c)

p	q	$p \Rightarrow q$	$\neg q \Rightarrow \neg p$	$(p \Rightarrow q) \Leftrightarrow (\neg q \Rightarrow \neg p)$
T	T	T	T	T
T	F	F	F	T
F	T	T	T	T
F	F	T	T	T

d)

p	$\neg p$	p NAND q
T	F	F
F	T	T

5. a) yes b) yes c) no

6. a) no b) yes c) yes

7. DeMorgan's Laws

p	q	$\neg(p \wedge q)$	$\neg p \vee \neg q$	$\neg(p \vee q)$	$\neg p \wedge \neg q$
T	T	F	F	F	F
T	F	T	T	F	F
F	T	T	T	F	F
F	F	T	T	T	T

8.

p	q	$p \vee q$	$\neg p \wedge \neg q$	$\neg(\neg p \wedge \neg q)$
T	T	T	F	T
T	F	T	F	T
F	T	T	F	T
F	F	F	T	F

9. F NAND (T NAND T) = T but (F NAND T) NAND T = F

10. a)

p	$\neg p$	$p \wedge \neg p$
T	F	F
F	T	F

b)

p	q	$p \wedge q$	$\neg p$	$p \wedge q \wedge \neg p$
T	T	T	F	F
T	F	F	F	F
F	T	F	T	F
F	F	F	T	F

c)

p	q	$p \wedge q$	$\neg(p \vee q)$	$p \wedge q \wedge \neg(p \vee q)$
T	T	T	F	F
T	F	F	F	F
F	T	F	F	F
F	F	F	T	F

d)

p	$\neg p$	$p \vee \neg p$	$\neg(p \vee \neg p)$
T	F	T	F
F	T	T	F

11. If p is T and q is F, then $p \Rightarrow q$ is F. But $\neg p$ is F, so $\neg p \Rightarrow \neg q$ is T. Therefore, $p \Rightarrow q$ and $\neg p \Rightarrow \neg q$ are not equivalent.

12. If p is T and q is F, then $p \Rightarrow q$ is F, but $q \Rightarrow p$ is T.

13. Yes; yes.

14. a)

p	q	r	$p \wedge (q \vee r)$
T	T	T	T
T	T	U	T
T	T	F	T
T	U	T	T
T	U	U	U
T	U	F	U
T	F	T	T
T	F	U	U
T	F	F	F
U	T	T	U
U	T	U	U
U	T	F	U
U	U	T	U
U	U	U	U
U	U	F	U
U	F	T	U
U	F	U	U
U	F	F	F
F	T	T	F
F	T	U	F
F	T	F	F
F	U	T	F
F	U	U	F
F	U	F	F
F	F	T	F
F	F	U	F
F	F	F	F

b)

p	q	$p \Rightarrow (q \vee \neg p)$
T	T	T
T	U	U
T	F	F
U	T	T
U	U	U
U	F	U
F	T	T
F	U	T
F	F	T

15. yes, yes

16. $\wedge$ distributes over $\underline{\vee}$ but $\underline{\vee}$ does not distribute over $\wedge$.

17. yes - F

18. $\neg(p \wedge \neg q) \wedge \neg(q \wedge \neg p)$

19. (p NAND p) NAND (q NAND q)

20. p NAND (q NAND q)

21. $p \vee q \Leftrightarrow \neg p \Rightarrow q$, $p \wedge q \Leftrightarrow \neg(\neg p \vee \neg q)$, and all connectives can be written in terms of $\wedge$, $\vee$, and $\neg$.

22. $\neg p \Leftrightarrow$ p NOR p, $p \vee q \Leftrightarrow \neg$(p NOR q), and all connectives can be written in terms of $\neg$ and $\vee$.

23. (p NOR p) NOR (q NOR q)

24. ((p NOR p) NOR q) NOR ((p NOR p) NOR q)

25. See solution to Exercise 9, Section 2.6.

Section 4.3

1. Not valid

2. Valid

3. Valid

4. Valid

5. Contraposition

6. If $p = q$, then $\sqrt{(pq)} = \sqrt{p^2} = p$ since $p > 0$, and

   $(p + q)/2 = (p + p)/2 = 2p/2 = p$

7. Let n be an even integer. Then $n = 2k$ for some integer k, and $n^2 = (2k)^2 = 4k^2 = 2(2k^2)$ which is even.

8. Suppose n is odd. Then $n = 2k + 1$ for some integer k. So $n^2 = (2k + 1)^2 = 4k^2 + 4k + 1 = 2(2k^2 + 2k) + 1$ which is odd, contradicting the assumption.

9. Let n and m be odd integers. Then $n = 2k + 1$ for some integer k, and $m = 2j + 1$ for some integer j. The product

$$\begin{aligned} nm &= (2k + 1)(2j + 1) \\ &= 4kj + 2k + 2j + 1 \\ &= 2(2kj + k + j) + 1 \text{ which is odd.} \end{aligned}$$

10. Suppose there is an odd integer solution, s. Then $s = 2k + 1$ for some integer k and

$0 = (2k + 1)^2 + (2k + 1) - n$

$= 4k^2 + 4k + 1 + 2k + 1 - n$

$= 4k^2 + 6k + 2 - n$

So $n = 4k^2 + 6k + 2 = 2(2k^2 + 3k + 1)$ which is even.

11. Suppose $f(x) = mx + b$ with $m \neq 0$. If $f(c) = f(d)$, then $mc + b = md + b$, so $mc = md$, and $c = d$.

12. Follows from Examples 4.36 and 4.35.

13. Assume that R is asymmetric. We have to show that, if x R y and y R x, then x = y. By asymmetry, the hypotheses "x R y and y R x" of this conditional is false; therefore the conditional "if x R y and y R x, then x = y" is true.

Section 4.4

1. { e, o }

2. { Lincoln, Garfield, McKinley, Kennedy }

3. The set of even integers.

4. a) { 4 } b) { 3, -2 }

5. Remainder of part 2 of theorem: If x is in the intersections of the truth-sets of P and Q, then both P(x) and Q(x) are true, so x is in the truth set of $P \wedge Q$.

   Part 3 of theorem: If x is an element of the truth-set of $P \vee Q$, then $(P \vee Q)(x)$ is true, that is, $P(x) \vee Q(x)$ is true. This means that at least one of P(x) and Q(x) are true, so x is an element of the union of the truth-sets of P and Q. Conversely, if x is in the union of the truth-sets of P and Q, then either x is in the truth set of P or of Q. In either case $(P \vee Q)(x)$ is true.

6. a) R

   b) $(-\infty,-1) \cup [1,\infty)$

7. a) $\{0\}$

   b) $(-\infty,1) \cup \{5\} \cup [7,8]$

8. ϕ

9.

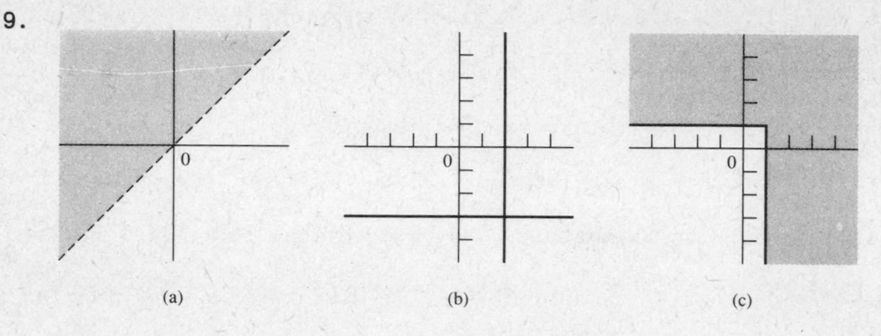

(a) (b) (c)

10. The truth-set of $P \Leftrightarrow Q$ is the complement of the symmetric difference $A \oplus B$ of the truth-sets A and B of P and Q, that is, $(A \oplus B)'$.

11. The truth-set of P NAND Q is the complement of the intersection of the truth-sets of P and Q.

12. The truth-set of P NOR Q is the complement of the union of the truth-sets of P and Q.

13. a) Equivalent b) Equivalent c) Not equivalent

14. $P(x) =$ "$x \in A$"

Section 4.5

1. a) $\exists n P(n)$ where $P(x) =$ "x is an even perfect number".

   b) $\forall P(Q(P) \Longrightarrow \exists x\, R(x,y))$ where $Q(x) =$ "x is a polynominal of odd degree" and $R(x,y)$ is "y is a root of the polynomial x".

   c) $\forall n(E(n)$ and $n > 2 \Longrightarrow \exists p \exists q(P(p) \wedge P(q) \wedge p + q = n))$ where $E(x)$ is "x is even" and $P(x) =$ "x is prime".

   d) $\forall f(I(f) \Longrightarrow N(f))$ where $I(f) =$ "f has an inverse" and $N(f) =$ "f is one-to-one".

2. a) $\exists R(P(R) \wedge \neg Q(R))$ where $P(x) =$ "x is transitive" and $Q(x) =$ "x

is reflexive".

b) $\forall x \exists N(1 + 1/2 + \ldots + 1/N > x)$

c) $\exists x \exists y(\ |x - y| < 0.005)$

d) $\forall \epsilon(\epsilon > 0 \Longrightarrow \exists \delta(\delta > 0 \wedge$

$\forall x \forall y(|x - y| < \delta \Longrightarrow |2x - 2y| < \epsilon)))$

3. a) Every integer is equal to itself; true.

   b) The equation $x^2 - x - 6 = 0$ has an integral solution; true.

   c) Every integer is either nonpositive or nonnegative; true.

   d) Every integer that is less than 0 is also less than 1; true.

4. a) There is an integer that is equal to 2 times itself; true.

   b) Every integer is a solution of $x^2 - x - 6 = 0$; false.

   c) Every integer greater than 5 is greater than 7; false.

   d) Every integer greater than 2 is composite; false.

5. If $\forall x[P(x) \Longleftrightarrow Q(x)]$ is true, then the truth-set of $P(x) \Longleftrightarrow Q(x)$ is X. If x is in the truth-set of P, then P(x) is T, so Q(x) is T, so x is in the truth-set of Q; and conversely. Now suppose that P and Q have the same truth-set A. If $x \in A$, then $P(x) \Longleftrightarrow Q(x)$ is $T \Longleftrightarrow T$ which is T; and if $x \notin A$, then $P(x) \Longleftrightarrow Q(x)$ is $F \Longleftrightarrow F$ which is T. Therefore, $\forall x[P(x) \Longleftrightarrow Q(x)]$ is true.

6. a) ϕ b) Z c) Z

7. a) ϕ b) R c) $(-1,0)$

8. a) T b) F c) F d) T e) F

9. a) F b) T c) F d) T e) T

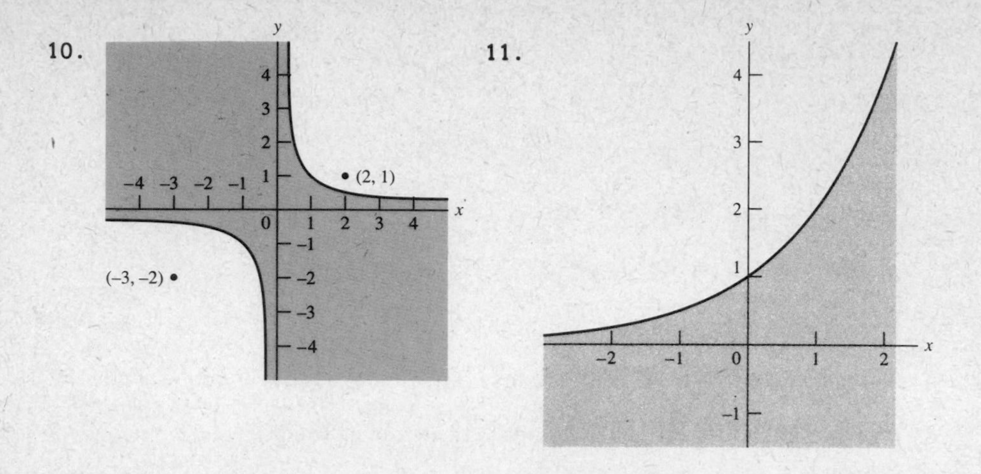

12. a) The truth-set of P is R x R.

b) The truth-set of P contains at least one point.

c) The truth-set of P contains a horizontal line and a vertical line.

13. a) If the truth-set of P contains a horizontal line, then it also contains a vertical line.

b) The truth-set of P contains the line $x = y$.

c) The truth-set of P is symmetric about the line $x = y$.

14. a) $P(x,y) = F$

b) $P(x,y) = F$

c) $P(x,y) = F$

15. a) $P(x,y) =$ "$y = 0$"

b) $P(x,y) = F$

c) $P(x,y) =$ "$y = 0$"

Section 4.6

1. a) $\forall x \; \underbrace{P(x,y)}_{f} \Rightarrow \exists y \; \underbrace{P(y,z)}_{f}$

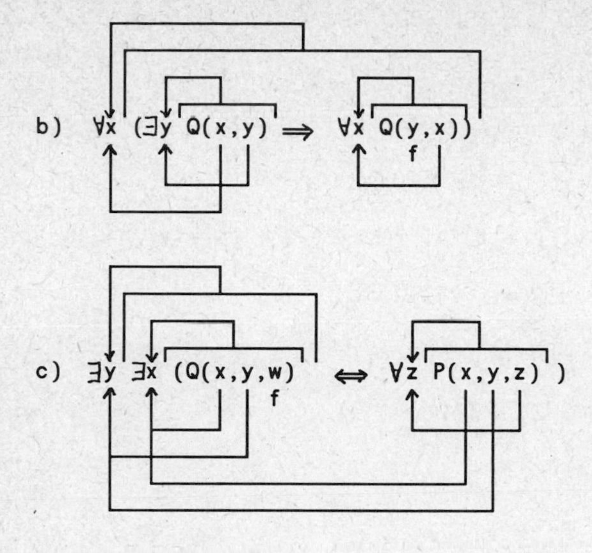

2.

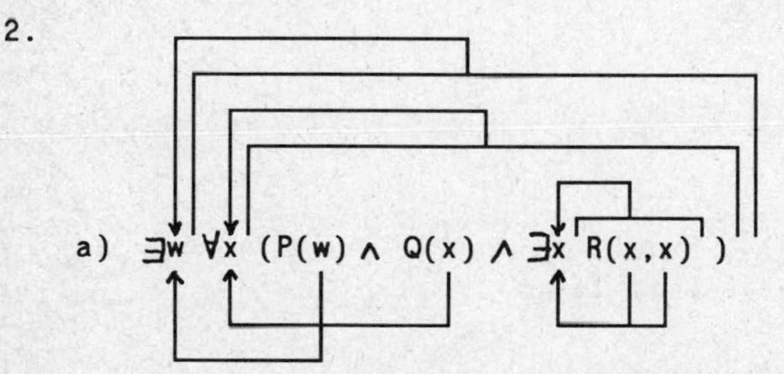

b) $P(x) \Rightarrow \exists x\ P(x)$
f

3. a) No; rule 3 violated; y is free in second formula.

   b) Yes

   c) Yes

4. a) Yes

   b) No; rule 3 violated; last occurrance of y is free in first formula but not in second.

   c) No; rule 4 violated.

5. a) $(\forall x \in A)\ (\exists y \in B)\ \ y^2 = x$

b) $(\exists x < 5)\ (\forall y > x)\ (2y > 1)$

c) $(\exists x < 0)\ (\exists y > 0)\ (xy = 5)$

6. a) $\exists x\{(x > 0) \wedge \exists y\ [(y > 0) \wedge$

$$\forall z\ ((z > 0) \Rightarrow (x - y < z))]\}$$

b) $\forall x\{(x \in Q) \Rightarrow \exists y[(y \in Z) \wedge \exists z((z \in Z) \wedge (x = y/z))]\}$

c) $\forall n\{(n \in Z) \Rightarrow \neg\exists m\ [(m \in Z) \wedge$

$$(\ (m^2 = n) \Rightarrow \neg\exists p((p \in Z) \wedge$$

$$\exists q((q \in Z) \wedge (p^2 = nq^2))))\ ]\}$$

7. a) $(x > y) \wedge (x^2 \leq z)$

b) $(x \geq y) \vee (x + y = 5)$

c) $(x < 7) \wedge (x \geq 3)$

d) $\exists x\ (x < 7)$

e) $\forall x\ (x \neq -1)$

8. a) $\exists x \forall y\ (xy \neq x)$

b) $\forall y \exists x\ (xy \neq x)$

c) $\forall x \exists y\ [(y < 0) \wedge (y^2 \neq x)]$

d) $\exists x \exists y \forall z\ [(x \geq z) \vee (z \geq y)]$

e) $(\exists x > 0)\ (\forall z > -1)\ [(z + x = 5) \wedge (z \geq x)]$

f) $(\exists x \in A)\ (\forall y \in B)\ (f(y) \neq x)$

9. a) $\exists x[\neg(x\ R\ x)]$

b) $\exists x \exists y[(x\ R\ y) \wedge \neg\ (y\ R\ x)]$

c) $\exists x \exists y \exists z[(x\ R\ y) \wedge (y\ R\ z) \wedge \neg(x\ R\ z)]$

Section 4.7

1. a) T b) F

2. a) F b) F

3. a) Not valid; $p = F$

b) Not valid; $p = F$, $q = T$

c) Not valid; $X = Z$, $P(x) =$ "$x = 0$", $x = 1$

d) Not valid; $X = Z$, $P(x) =$ "$x = 0$", $x = 0$, $y = 1$

4. a) Not valid; $X = Z$, $P(x) =$ "$x = 0$", $Q(x) =$ "$x = 1$", $x = 0$

   b) Not valid; $X = Z$, $P(x) =$ "$x = 0$", $Q(x) =$ "$x = 0$", $x = 1$

   c) Not valid; $X = Z$, $P(x) =$ "$x = 0$", $x = 0$

   d) Valid

5. a) Not valid; $X = Z$, $P(x) =$ "$x = 1$", $Q(x) =$ "$x = 2$"

   b) Not valid; $X = R$, $P(x,y) =$ "$x = y$"

   c) Not valid; $X = Z$, $P(x) =$ "$x = 1$"

   d) Not valid; $X = Z$, $P(x) =$ "$x = 1$"

6. All are valid.

7. Case 1: the truth set of P is a subset of the truth set of Q. In this case, $\forall x[P(x) \Rightarrow Q(x)]$ is T, and the formula is then equivalent to $P(y) \Rightarrow Q(y)$, which is true in this case.

   Case 2: the truth set of P is not a subset of the truth set of Q. In this case, $\forall x[P(x) \Rightarrow Q(x)]$ is F so the truth-value of the formula is T.

8. To represent the statement correctly, let $P(n) =$ "n is even", $Q(n) =$ "n is prime", and $R(n) =$ "$n = 2$". Then the statement is written

$$(\forall n \in N)[(Q(n) \land P(n)) \Rightarrow R(n)]$$

   It is not valid to infer

$$(\forall n \in N)[Q(n) \Rightarrow R(n)] \lor (\forall n \in N)[P(n) \Rightarrow R(n)]$$

   because

$$\forall n[Q(n) \land P(n) \Rightarrow R(n)] \Rightarrow \forall n[Q(n) \Rightarrow R(n)] \lor \forall n[P(n) \Rightarrow R(n)]$$

   is not a valid formula of predicate logic.

Chapter Review

1. a) 6 is not a perfect number and 6 is prime.

   b) 6 is not a perfect number.

   c) 6 is not prime nor is 6 a perfect number.

   d) If 6 is a perfect number, then 6 is prime.

2. a) $p \Rightarrow q$ b) $p \Rightarrow q$ c) $p \Rightarrow \neg q$

3.

p	q	$p \Rightarrow q$	$p \wedge (p \Rightarrow q) \vee q$
T	T	T	T
T	F	F	F
F	T	T	T
F	F	T	F

4. a) tautology b) tautology c) tautology d) neither

5. a) tautology b) neither c) neither d) tautology

6. a) $\neg(p \vee p) \vee p$

   b) $\neg(\neg q \vee r) \vee [\neg(p \vee q) \vee (p \vee r)]$

   c) $\neg[p \vee (q \vee r)] \vee [q \vee (p \vee r)]$

7. a) $\neg[\neg(\neg p \vee q) \vee \neg r]$ b) $\neg(\neg p \vee \neg q) \vee r$

   c) $\neg[\neg(p \vee \neg(\neg p \vee q)) \vee (\neg(\neg p \vee q) \vee \neg p)]$

8. a) [(p NAND p) NAND (q NAND q)] NAND (p NAND p)

   b) [(p NOR q) NOR p] NOR [(p NOR q) NOR p]

9.

	converse	inverse	contrapositive
a)	$p \Rightarrow q$	$\neg q \Rightarrow \neg p$	$\neg p \Rightarrow \neg q$
b)	$\neg q \Rightarrow \neg p$	$p \Rightarrow q$	$q \Rightarrow p$
c)	$\neg p \Rightarrow \neg q$	$q \Rightarrow p$	$p \Rightarrow q$
d)	$\neg q \Rightarrow p$	$\neg p \Rightarrow q$	$q \Rightarrow \neg p$

10. The inverse of $p \Rightarrow q$ is $\neg p \Rightarrow \neg q$, and the converse of the inverse is $\neg q \Rightarrow \neg p$, which is the contrapositive of the original implication.

11. (T NOR T) NOR F = T but T NOR (T NOR F) = F.

12. valid

13. direct proof

14. Let n and m be odd integers. Then n and m can be written respectively as $2k + 1$ and $2l + 1$, for some integers k and l. So the sum

$$\begin{aligned} n + m &= (2k + 1) + (2l + 1) \\ &= 2k + 2l + 2 \\ &= 2(k + l + 1) \text{ which is even} \end{aligned}$$

15. Let p and q be rational numbers. Then $p = a/b$ and $q = c/d$, where a,b,c, and d are integers. Then

$p + q = a/b + c/d = (ad + cb)/bd = m/n$ for some integers m and n.

16. $\{ n, w, p \}$

17. $\{ \ldots, -8, -7, -3, -2, 2, 3, 7, 8, \ldots \}$

18. a) $(-2,8)$ b) $\{ 0 \}$

19. a) $(-\infty,-1)$ b) $[-1,1]$

20.

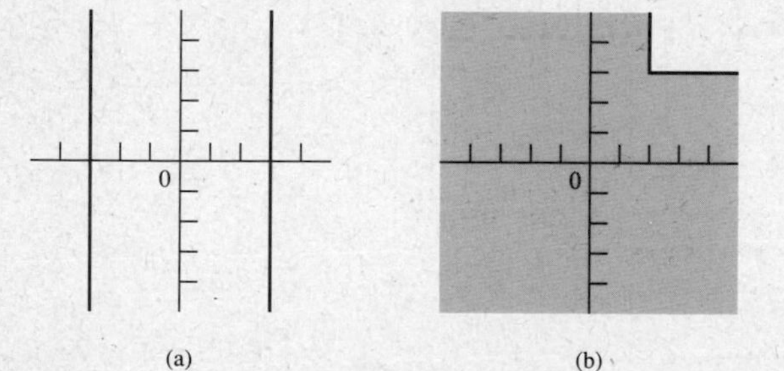

(a) (b)

21. a) $\exists z(xz = y)$ b) $\forall a \forall b(a \, R \, b \Rightarrow b \, R \, a)$

c) $(\forall \epsilon > 0)(\exists \delta > 0)\forall x[\, 0 < |x - a| < \delta \Rightarrow |f(x) - b| < \epsilon \,]$

22. a) F b) F c) T d) T

23. a) $\exists x(x \, R \, x)$

b) $\exists x \exists y[(x \, R \, y) \wedge (y \, R \, z) \wedge (x \neq y)]$

c) $\exists x \exists y[(x \, R \, y) \wedge (y \, R \, x)]$

24. a) T b) T c) F d) T

25. a) T b) T c) T

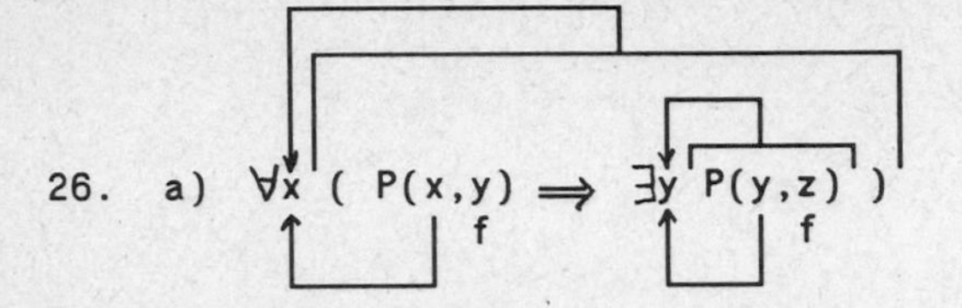

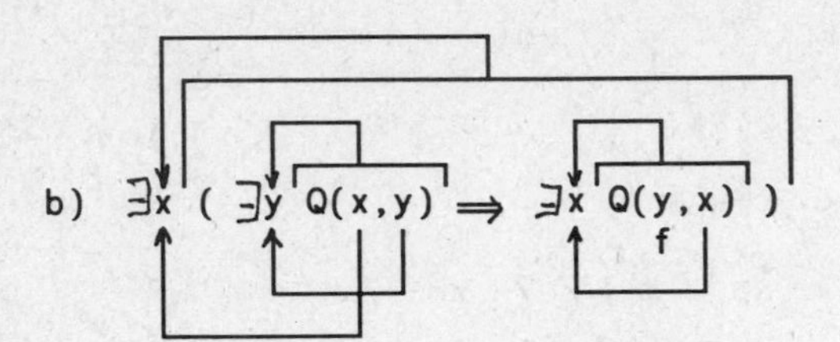

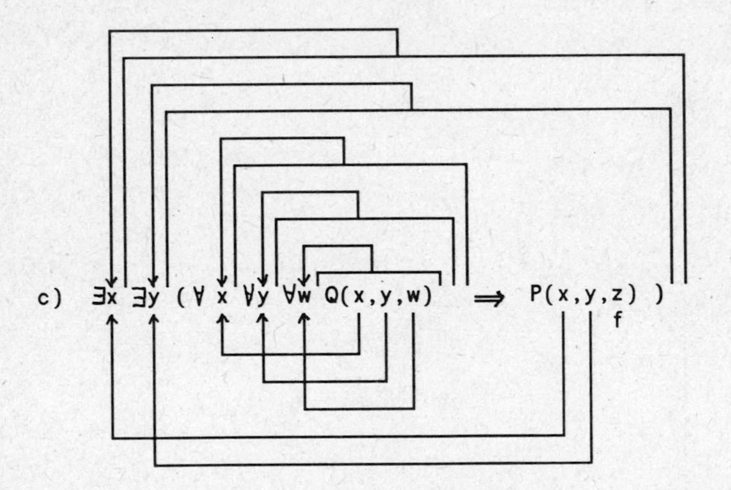

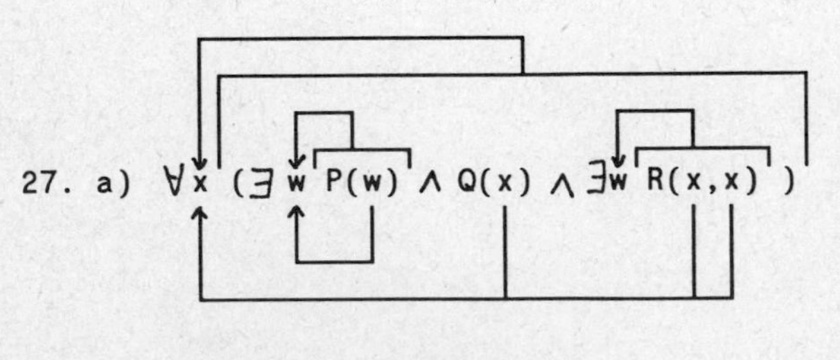

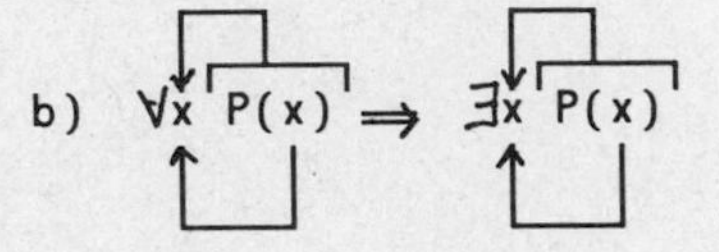

28. a) No; rule 3 violated; y is free in second formula.

    b) No; rule 2 violated.

29. a) No; rule 2 violated.

    b) Yes

30. a) $(\forall x>5)(\exists y<2)\ (y = x^2)$

    b) $(\exists x \in C)(\forall y>x)\ (2y > 1)$

    c) $(\forall x<0)(\forall y>0)\ (x + y = -1)$

31. a) $\exists x\{\ x \in A \wedge \exists y[y \in B \wedge \forall z(z > 5 \Rightarrow\ x + y = z)]\}$

    b) $\forall x\{\ x \in Z \Rightarrow\ \exists y[\ y \in N \wedge \exists z(\ z \in N \wedge x = y - z)]\}$

32. a) $(x > y) \wedge (x < z)$

    b) $(x \neq y) \wedge (x - y \geq 5)$

    c) $(x < 7) \vee (x \geq 3)$

33. a) $\exists y\ (y \geq 17)$

    b) $\forall z\ (z^2 \neq -1)$

    c) $\forall x \exists y\ (x + y \leq y)$

    d) $\exists y \forall x\ (x \leq y^2 + 1)$

34. a) F b) T c) F

35. a) Not valid; p = T

    b) Valid

    c) Not valid; set = { 0 }, P(0) = F, x = 0

36. a) Not valid; set = { 0 }, P(0) = T, x = y = 0

    b) Not valid; set = { 0 }, P(0) = F, x = 0

    c) Not valid; set = { 0 }, P(0) = T, x = 0

Chapter 5

Section 5.1

1. No; addition does not distribute over multiplication.

2. No divisor x satisfies both g.c.d.(x,6) = 1 and l.c.m.(x,6) = 12.

3. $2(8)(8) + 2(8)(8)(8) + 2(8)(8)(8) = 2{,}176$

4. g.c.d.: 1; l.c.m.: N

5. If 0_a and 0_b are identities for v, then

   $0_a = 0_b \vee 0_a = 0_a \vee 0_b = 0_b$

6. Both $0' = 1$ and $1' = 0$ mean that $0 \vee 1 = 1$ and $0 \wedge 1 = 0$; these are true because 0 and 1 are identities for v and $\wedge$ respectively.

7. a) $(x \vee 0) \wedge (y \wedge 1)$ b) $[(x \vee y) \wedge z]'$

8. a) $(x \vee 1) \vee (x \vee 0)$ b) $(x \vee y \vee 0)' \wedge (z \wedge 1)'$

9. $x \vee x = (x \vee x) \wedge 1 = (x \vee x) \wedge (x \vee x')$

   $= x \vee (x \wedge x') = x \vee 0 = x$

10. $x \vee 1 = (x \vee 1) \wedge 1 = (x \vee 1) \wedge (x \vee x')$

    $= x \vee (1 \wedge x') = x \vee x' = 1$

11. $(x \wedge y) \wedge (x' \vee y') = [(x \wedge y) \wedge x'] \vee [(x \wedge y) \wedge y']$

    $= [(x \wedge x') \wedge y] \vee [(y \wedge y') \wedge x]$

    $= [0 \wedge y] \vee [0 \wedge x]$

    $= 0 \vee 0 = 0$

12. $(x \vee y) \wedge (x' \wedge y') = [x \wedge (x' \wedge y')] \vee [y \wedge (x' \wedge y')]$

    $= [(x \wedge x') \wedge y'] \vee [(y \wedge y') \wedge x']$

    $= [0 \wedge y'] \vee [0 \wedge x']$

    $= 0 \vee 0 = 0$

    $(x \vee y) \vee (x' \wedge y') = [(x \vee y) \vee x'] \wedge [(x \vee y) \vee y']$

    $= [(x \vee x') \vee y] \wedge [(y \vee y') \vee x]$

    $= [1 \vee y] \wedge [1 \vee x]$

$= 1 \wedge 1 = 1$

13. a) $x \wedge (x \vee y) = (x \vee 0) \wedge (x \vee y)$

$= x \vee (0 \wedge y) = x \vee 0 = x$

b) $x \vee (x \wedge y) = (x \wedge 1) \vee (x \wedge y)$

$= x \wedge (1 \vee y) = x \wedge 1 = x$

14.

	lub	glb
a)	a and b	none
b)	c and d	none
c)	a and b	f and l
d)	d	k

15.

	lub	glb
a)	a	j
b)	c	k
c)	none	f
d)	c	none

16.

	lub	glb
a)	10	1
b)	15	1
c)	30	1
d)	60	2

17.

	lub	glb
a)	10	1
b)	6	3
c)	35	1
d)	42	1

18. $\text{lub}(A,B) = A \cup B$; $\text{glb}(A,B) = A \cap B$

19. No; some glb's do not exist; lub's are not unique.

20. No; some glb's and lub's do not exist.

21. Yes.

22. The distributive law: $b \wedge (e \vee c) = b \wedge a = b$

but $(b \wedge e) \vee (b \wedge c) = d \vee c = c$

23. 2, 3, 5

24.

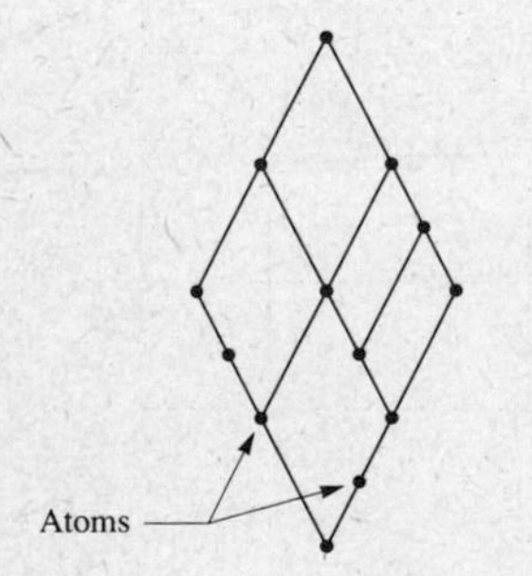

25. i, j, k

26. a) none; none b) none; none

27. a) 1 and a b) 1; none

28. a) If a and b are both universal lower bounds, then $a \leq b$ and $b \leq a$ so $a = b$. Part b) is similar.

29. If $x \leq y$ then $x = x \wedge y$ by definition, so that

$$y \vee x = y \vee (x \wedge y) = (1 \wedge y) \vee (x \wedge y) = (1 \vee x) \wedge y = 1 \wedge y = y$$

showing that $x \# y$. The converse is similar.

30. a) Yes b) No c) Yes

31. a) No b) Yes c) Yes

32. Counterexample: Let $L = D_{30}$ and $M = \{ 1, 2, 5, 30 \}$.

l.c.m(2,5) = 10 $\notin$ M

Section 5.2

1. a) No b) Yes

2. a) Yes b) No

3. f: $x\bar{y} \vee \overline{xy}$ g: $x\bar{y} \vee \bar{x}y$

4. a) $xy \vee x\bar{y} \vee \overline{xy}$ b) $xy \vee \overline{xy}$

5. $x\overline{yz} \vee \bar{x}yz \vee \bar{x}y\bar{z} \vee \overline{xyz}$

6. $xyz \vee xy\bar{z} \vee \bar{x}yz \vee \overline{xyz}$

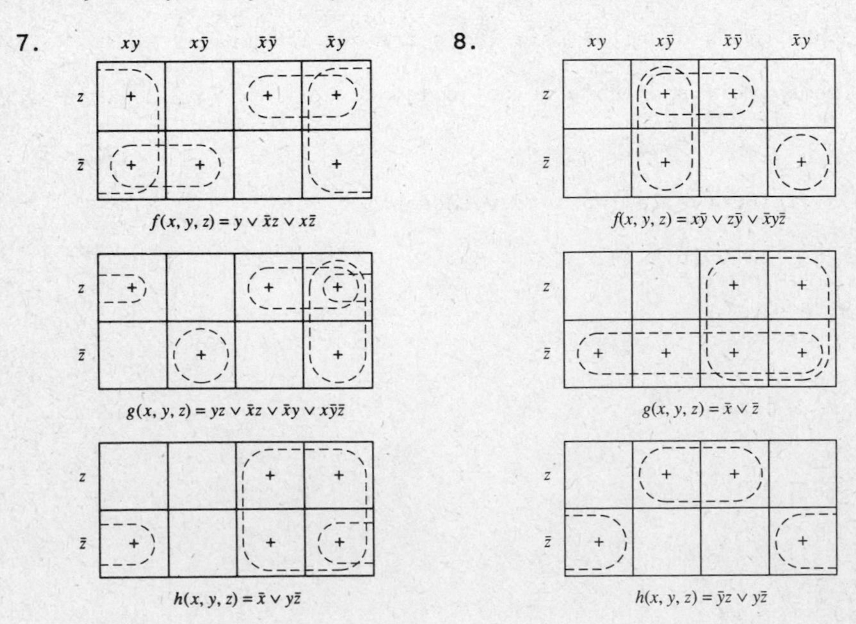

7. $f(x, y, z) = y \vee \bar{x}z \vee x\bar{z}$

$g(x, y, z) = yz \vee \bar{x}z \vee \bar{x}y \vee x\bar{y}\bar{z}$

$h(x, y, z) = \bar{x} \vee y\bar{z}$

8. $f(x, y, z) = x\bar{y} \vee z\bar{y} \vee \bar{x}y\bar{z}$

$g(x, y, z) = \bar{x} \vee \bar{z}$

$h(x, y, z) = \bar{y}z \vee y\bar{z}$

9.

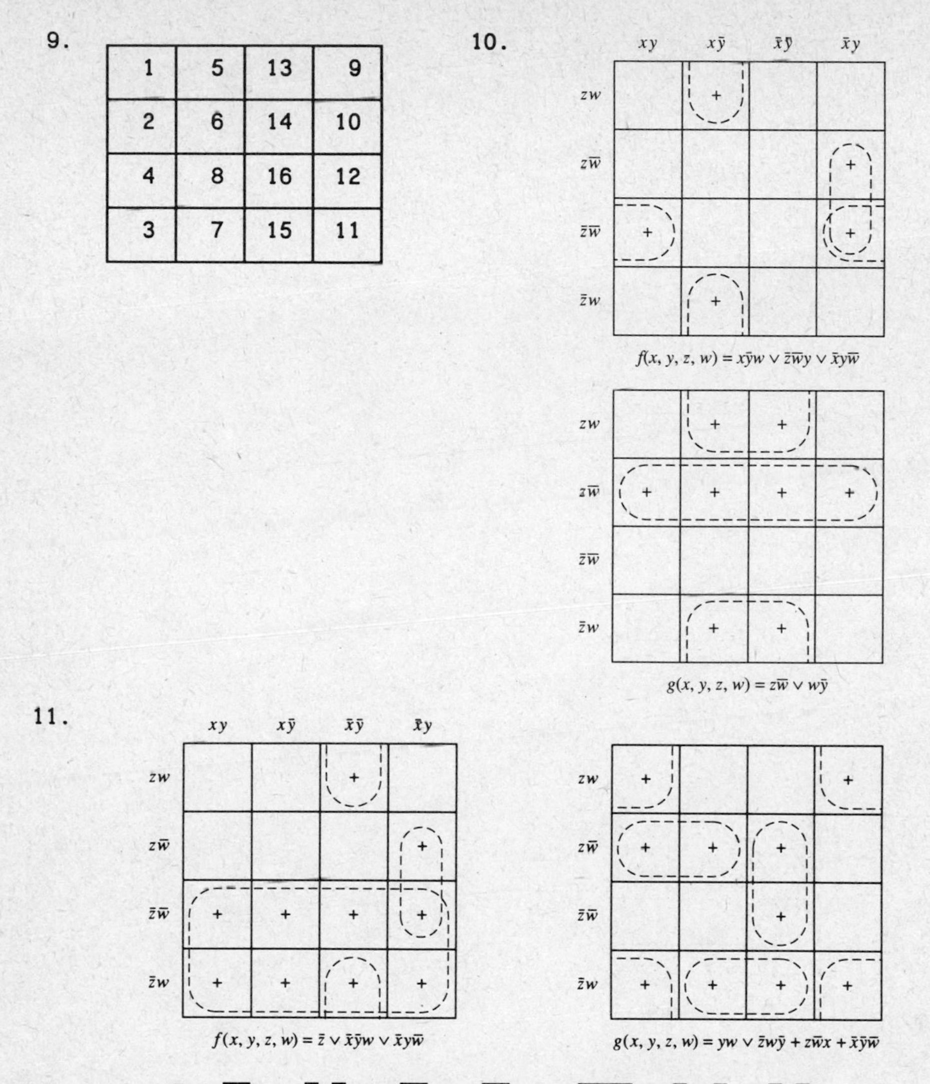

1	5	13	9
2	6	14	10
4	8	16	12
3	7	15	11

$f(x, y, z, w) = x\bar{y}w \vee \bar{z}\bar{w}y \vee \bar{x}y\bar{w}$

$g(x, y, z, w) = z\bar{w} \vee w\bar{y}$

$f(x, y, z, w) = \bar{z} \vee \bar{x}\bar{y}w \vee \bar{x}y\bar{w}$

$g(x, y, z, w) = yw \vee \bar{z}w\bar{y} + z\bar{w}x + \bar{x}\bar{y}\bar{w}$

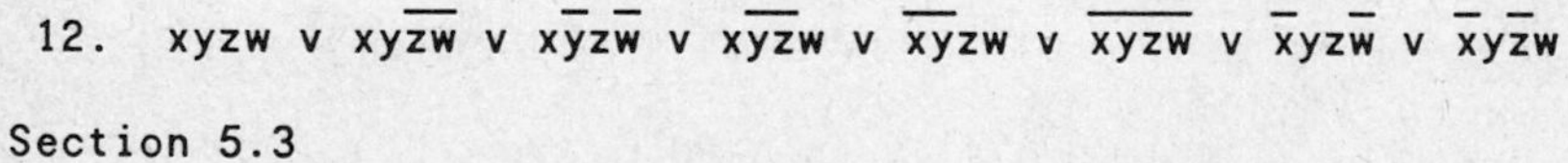

12. $xyzw \vee xy\overline{zw} \vee x\bar{y}z\bar{w} \vee x\overline{yz}w \vee \overline{xy}zw \vee \overline{xyzw} \vee \bar{x}yz\bar{w} \vee \bar{x}y\bar{z}w$

Section 5.3

1. a) Output = ¬x ∧ ¬y where x and y are the inputs.

   It is equivalent to (b).

   b) Output = ¬x v ¬y where x and y are the inputs.

   It is equivalent to (d).

2. a) ¬x v y   b) (x ∧ ¬y) v (¬x ∧ y)

   c) (x ∧ y) v ¬(x v y)   d) (x ∧ y) v (x v y)

3.

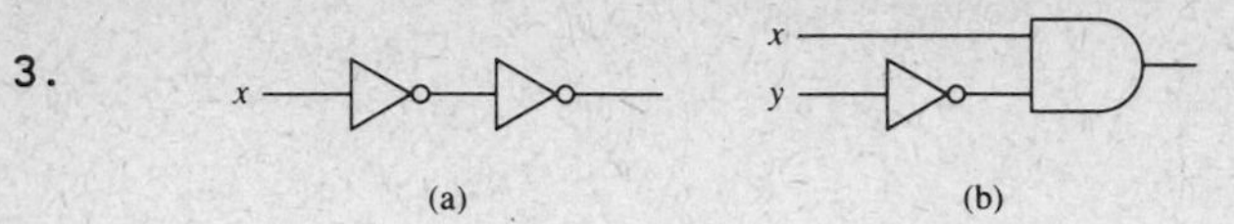

(a) (b)

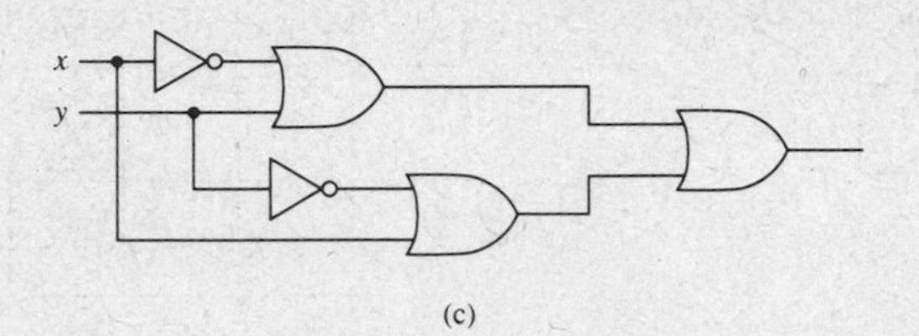

(c)

4.

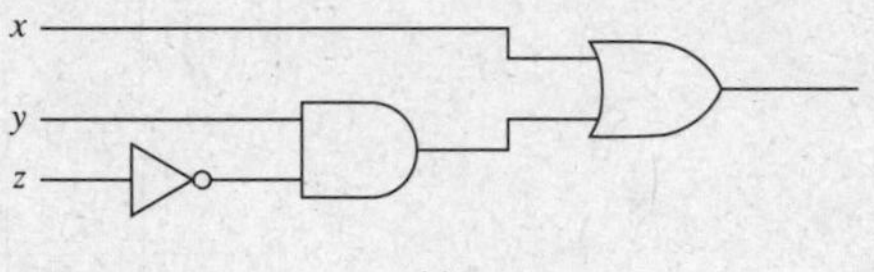

(a)

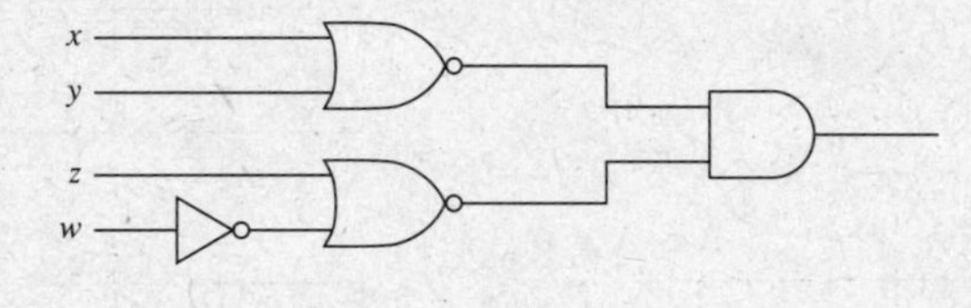

(b)

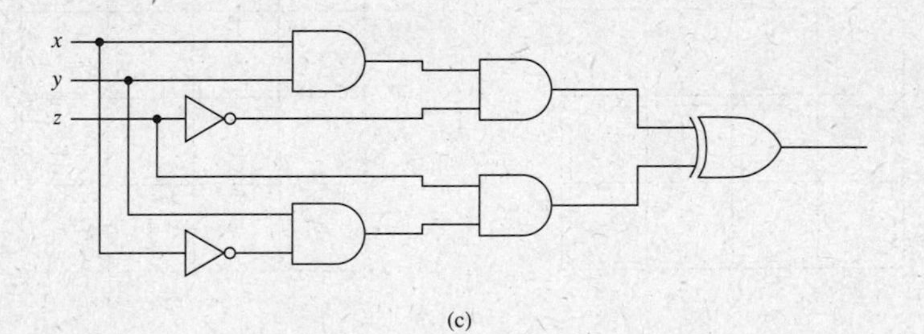

(c)

5. a) $\neg x \veebar \neg y$ b) (x NAND y) $\vee$ (y NAND z)

6. a) $(\neg p \wedge q \wedge r) \vee (p \wedge \neg q \wedge r) \vee (p \wedge \neg q \wedge \neg r)$

b) $\neg[(p \wedge q) \vee (r \wedge s) \vee (t \wedge u)]$

7.

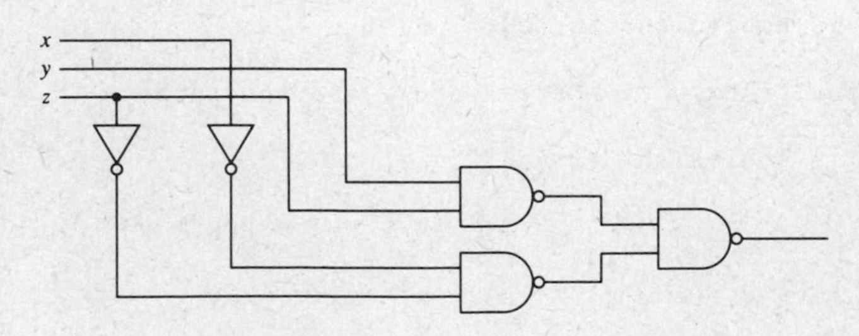

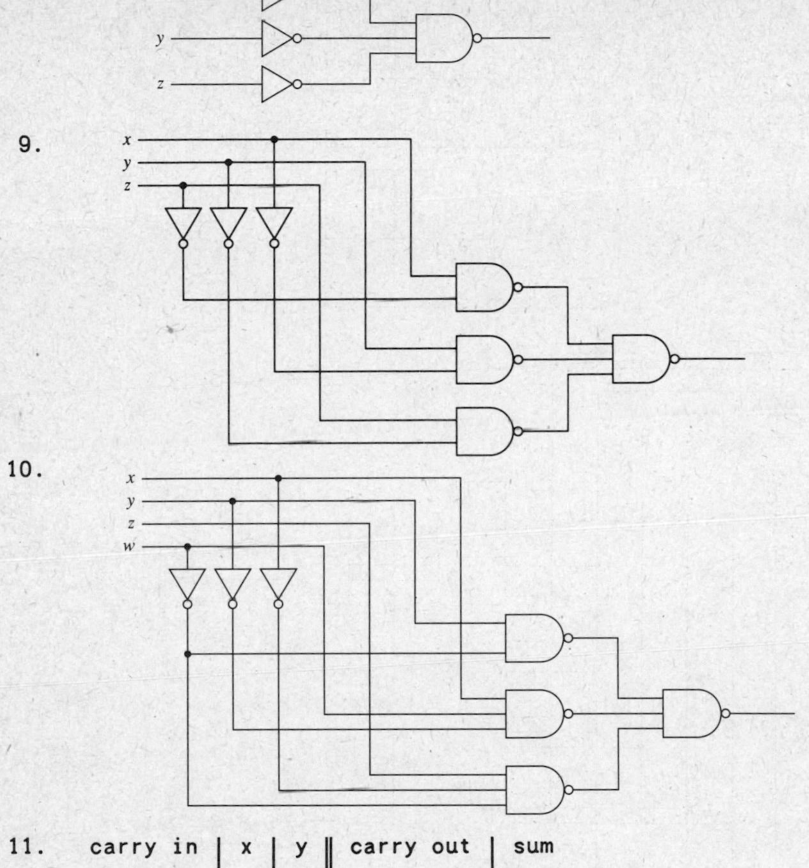

11.

carry in	x	y	carry out	sum
1	1	1	1	1
1	1	0	1	0
1	0	1	1	0
1	0	0	0	1
0	1	1	1	0
0	1	0	0	1
0	0	1	0	1
0	0	0	0	0

12.

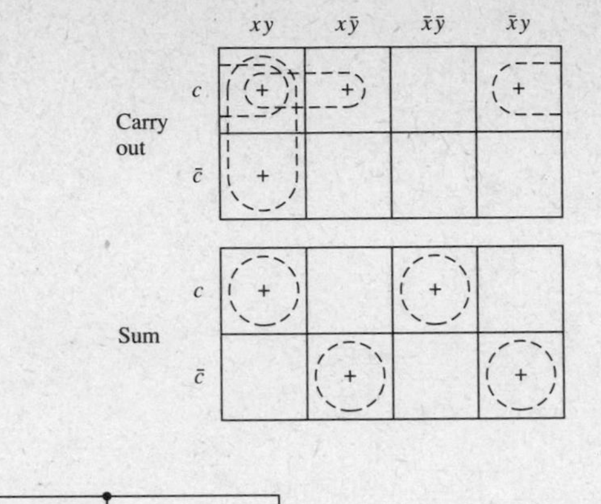

xy
$x\bar{y}$
$\bar{x}\bar{y}$
$\bar{x}y$
Carry
out
c
$\bar{c}$
Sum
c
$\bar{c}$

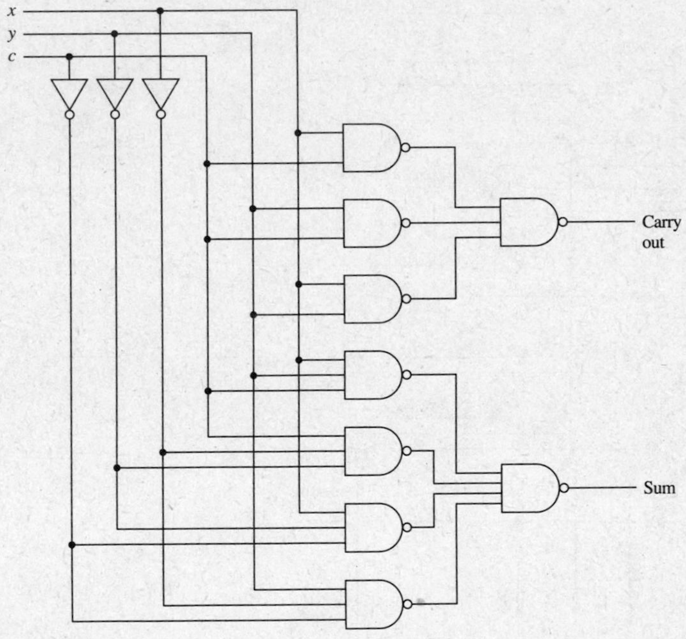

x
y
c
Carry
out
Sum

Section 5.4

1.

s	r	q	q'	$\neg(s \wedge q')$	$\neg(r \wedge q)$	$q \Leftrightarrow \neg(s \wedge q')$	$q' \Leftrightarrow \neg(r \wedge q)$
T	T	T	T	F	F	F	F
T	T	T	F	T	F	T	T
T	T	F	T	F	T	T	T
T	T	F	F	T	T	F	F
T	F	T	T	F	T	F	T
T	F	T	F	T	T	T	F
T	F	F	T	F	T	T	T
T	F	F	F	T	T	F	F
F	T	T	T	T	F	T	F
F	T	T	F	T	F	T	T
F	T	F	T	T	T	F	T
F	T	F	F	T	T	F	F
F	F	T	T	T	T	T	T
F	F	T	F	T	T	T	F
F	F	F	T	T	T	F	T
F	F	F	F	T	T	F	F

2. a) $y = x \wedge y$. The solutions are:

x	y
T	T
T	F
F	F

b) $y = \neg(x \wedge y)$. The solutions are:

x	y
F	T

c) The output oscillates between T and F.

3. a) $q = \neg(q' \wedge \neg(d \quad c))$; $q' = \neg(q \wedge \neg(\neg d \wedge c))$

b)

c	d	s	r	q	q'
T	T	F	T	T	F
T	F	T	F	F	T
F	T	T	T	T	F
F	T	T	T	F	T
F	F	T	T	T	F
F	F	T	T	F	T

Chapter Review

1. a) $(x \vee y') \wedge (z \vee 0)'$ b) $\neg(p \wedge T) \vee (F \wedge q)$

c) $(A \cap B)' \cup C$

2. a) $\neg(\neg(x \wedge y)) = \neg(\neg x \vee \neg y)$ b) $p \vee T = T$

c) $A \cap X = A$

3. Always.

4. When it has at most two elements, otherwise, an element other than the maximal and minimal element has no complement.

5. a) Yes

   b) lub(z,w) is the complex number at the upper right corner of the rectangle (having sides parallel to the axes) with corners at z and w; glb(z,w) is the lower left corner of the same rectangle.

   c) No; there are no identity elements for the operations of lub and glb.

6. a) No; any set $\{ 1, 2, 3, x \}$, where $x > 3$, is a lub of $\{ 1, 2 \}$ and $\{ 1, 3 \}$.

7. To say that $x \vee y$ is the unique least upper bound of x and y means (a) $x \leq x \vee y$, (b) $y \leq x \vee y$, and (c) if $x \leq w$ and $y \leq w$ then $x \vee y \leq w$.

   a) $x \leq x \vee y$ means $x = x \wedge (x \vee y)$, which is true because it is one of the absorption laws.

   b) is similar to a)

   c) The statement to be proved means, if $x = x \wedge w$ and $y = y \wedge w$, then $x \vee y = (x \vee y) \wedge w$. If $x = x \wedge w$ and $y = y \wedge w$, then $x \vee y = (x \wedge w) \vee (y \wedge w) = (x \vee y) \wedge w$ by the distributive law. The greatest lower bound part is even simpler:

   a) $x \wedge y \leq x$ means $x \wedge y = (x \wedge y) \wedge x$ which is true by the idempotent law;

   b) $x \wedge y \leq y$ is similar;

   c) If $w \leq x$ and $w \leq y$, then $w = w \wedge x$ and $w = w \wedge y$, so $w = w$

   $w = (w \wedge x) \wedge (w \wedge y) = w \wedge (x \wedge y)$ which means that $w \leq x \wedge y$.

8. a) Yes b) Yes c) No

9. a) $xy\overline{z} \vee x\overline{yz} \vee \overline{xyz} \vee \overline{xy}z \vee \overline{x}y\overline{z}$

b) $pqr \vee \overline{p}qr \vee \overline{p}q\overline{r} \vee \overline{pq}r \vee \overline{pqr}$

10. a) $\overline{z} \vee \overline{xy}$ b) $\overline{p} \vee qr$

11. a) $[(p \underline{\vee} q) \underline{\vee} r] \underline{\vee} s$ b) $(\neg p \vee p) \wedge p$

c) $(p \text{ NOR } q) \text{ NOR } (\neg r \text{ NOR } q) \text{ NOR } (\neg p \text{ NOR } q)$

12.

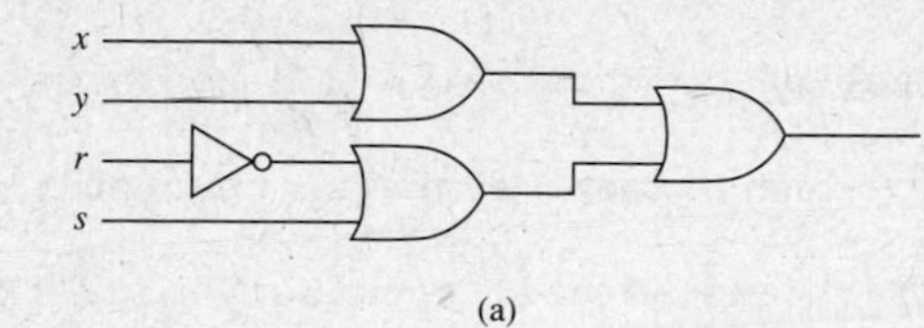

(a)

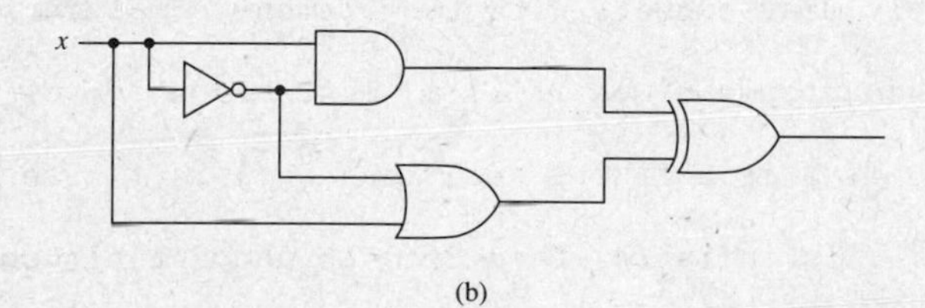

(b)

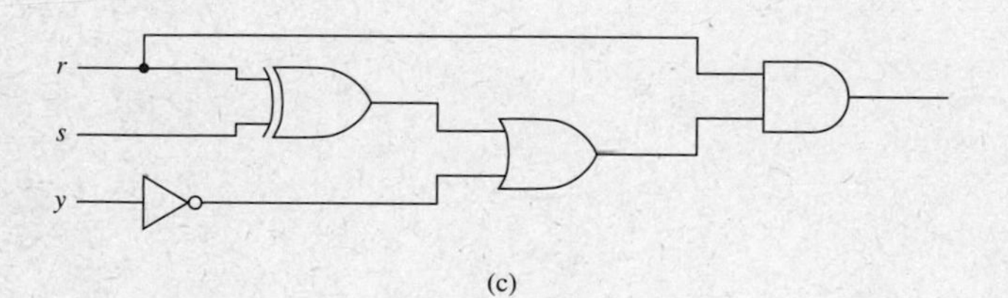

(c)

13. It is an S-R flip-flop.

14. It generates a true-going pulse (false to true to false transition) whenever the input changes. The length of the pulse is approximately four gate delays.

15. $q = \neg(s \wedge q')$

$q' = \neg(r \wedge q)$

$y = \neg(x \wedge s)$

$s = \neg(y \wedge c)$

$r = \neg(s \wedge c \wedge x)$

$x = \neg(r \wedge d)$

The solutions are

c	d	x	y	s	r	q	q'
T	T	F	T	F	T	T	F
T	T	T	F	T	F	F	T
T	F	T	F	T	F	F	T
T	F	T	T	F	T	T	F
F	T	F	T	T	T	T	F
F	T	F	T	T	T	F	T
F	F	T	F	T	T	T	F
F	F	T	F	T	T	F	T

16. a) It suffices to show that B is closed under the operations of union and intersection. If A and B are finite, then $A \cup B$ and $A \cap B$ are finite. If A and B have finite complements, so do $A \cup B$ and $A \cap B$ because $(A \cup B)' = A' \cap B'$ and $(A \cap B)' = A' \cup B'$. If A is finite and B has a finite complement, then $A \cap B$ is finite because it is a subset of A, and $A \cup B$ has a finite complement because it is a superset of B, that is, $A \cup B$ contains B.

b) N has countably many one-element subsets, countably many subsets with one-element complements, countably many two-element subsets, countably many subsets with two-element complements, etc. Therefore, B is countable since it is a countable union of countable sets. If Y is a finite set, then P(Y) is finite so $P(Y) \neq B$; but if Y is infinite, then P(Y) is uncountable so $P(Y) \neq B$.

Chapter 6

Section 6.1

1. 35,536 2. 27 3. 5^{20} 4. n^k

5. The total possible two- and three-letter initials is $(26)^2 + (26)^3 = 18{,}252 < 18{,}273$; apply the Pigeonhole Principle.

6. a) 6561 b) 328.05 minutes c) 4608

7. $(100)^5$ 8. 60,840

9. $[(26)^3 - 137](10)^3 + (26)^2(10)^4 = 24{,}199{,}000$

10. $[(26)^2 + (26)^3 + (26)^4 + (26)^5](27)(10)^4(26) = 86{,}743{,}360{,}080{,}000$

11. 2,598,960 12. 2,193,360

13. For each of the n elements there are two choices: it is in the subset or it isn't. So there are $2 \times 2 \times \ldots \times 2 = 2^n$ subsets.

14. 6 15. a) 4 b) 6

16. a) 15 b) 15 c) 45

17. a) 99 b) 8 c) 9 d) 12

18. $n(A \cup B \cup C \cup D) = n(A) + n(B) + n(C) + n(D) - n(A \cap B)$

$- n(A \cap C) - n(A \cap D) - n(B \cap C) - n(B \cap D) - n(C \cap D)$

$+ n(A \cap B \cap C) + n(A \cap B \cap D) + n(A \cap C \cap D)$

$+ n(B \cap C \cap D) - n(A \cap B \cap C \cap D)$

19. 2^{n^2-n} 20. $2^{(n^2+n)/2}$

21. Step 1: The formula holds for two sets. Step 2: assume that the formula holds for n sets. Let $A = \bigcup_{i=1}^{n} A_i$ and let the (n+1)st set be B. Then by the distributive law,

$$A \cap B = (\cup A_i) \cap B = \cup (A_i \cap B)$$

By the induction hypotheses,

$n(A) = \Sigma\, n(A_i) - \Sigma\, n(A_i \cap A_j) + \Sigma\, (A_i \cap A_j \cap A_k) - \ldots$

and

$n(\cup(A_i \cap B)) = \Sigma\, n(A_i \cap B) - \Sigma\, n(A_i \cap A_j \cap B) + \ldots$

Therefore,

$$\begin{aligned} n(A \cup B) &= n(A) + n(B) - n(A \cap B) \\ &= \Sigma\, n(A_i) - \Sigma\, n(A_i \cap A_j) + \Sigma\, (A_i \cap A_j \cap A_k) - \ldots \\ &\quad + n(B) - n(\cup(A_i \cap B)) \\ &= \Sigma\, n(A_i) - \Sigma\, n(A_i \cap A_j) + \Sigma\, (A_i \cap A_j \cap A_k) - \ldots \\ &\quad + n(B) - \Sigma\, n(A_i \cap B) + \Sigma\, n(A_i \cap A_j \cap B) - \ldots \end{aligned}$$

which is the inclusion-exclusion formula for the sets $A_1, \ldots, A_n, B$.

Section 6.2

1. a) 4 b) 20 c) 1 d) 362,880

2. 720 3. 30,240; 27,216 4. P(m,k)

5. 35,880,000; 32,292,000 6. $(8!)^5$

7. 18!; 18! − 2(17!) = 16(17!) 8. 720

9. 181,440; 840 10. 483,840 11. 696,729,600

12. 7!/(2!2!) = 1260 13. 7!/2! = 2520 14. 26^3; 26^3

15. If n is even : $26^{n/2}$; if n is odd: $26^{(n+1)/2}$

Section 6.3

1. a) 3 b) 56 c) 1 d) 6

2. $$C(52,5) = \frac{48 \times 49 \times 50 \times 51 \times 52}{1 \times 2 \times 3 \times 4 \times 5}$$

= 48 / 1 x 49 / 2 x 50 / 3 x 51 / 4 x 52 / 5

= 48 x 49 / 2 x 50 / 3 x 51 / 4 x 52 / 5

= 2352 / 2 x 50 / 3 x 51 / 4 x 52 / 5

= 1176 x 50 / 3 x 51 / 4 x 52 / 5

= ...

= 2,598,960

3. C(n,n−1) = n!/(n−1)![n−(n−1)]!

= n!/(n−1)!(1!)

= n!/(n−1)!

= n(n−1)!/(n−1)!

= n

4. C(n,r) is the number of r-element subsets in a set of n elements. The number of ways to choose r elements to put in a subset is the same as the number of ways to choose the (n − r) elements of the complement. Thus, C(n,r) = C(n,n−r).

5. 31,824 6. 28 7. C(52,13) 8. 108

9. 186^{80} 10. 128

11. a) C(12,4)C(8,4) = 34,650 b) 3C(8,4) = 210

c) (3)(2)C(10,3)C(7,3) = 25,200

12. 314; 314

13. $C(n-1,r-1) = (n-1)!/(r-1)![n-1-(r-1)]!$

$= (n-1)!/(r-1)!(n-r)!$

and $C(n-1,r) = (n-1)!/r!(n-1-r)!$

$= (n-1)!/r!(n-r-1)!$

So $C(n-1,r-1) + C(n-1,r)$

$$= \frac{(n-1)!r!(n-r-1)! + (n-1)!(r-1)!(n-r)!}{(r-1)!(n-r)!r!(n-r-1)!}$$

Since $r! = r(r-1)!$ and $(n-r)! = (n-r)(n-r-1)!$, the sum can

be written as $\dfrac{(n-1)!(r-1)!(n-r-1)![r + (n-r)]}{(r-1)!(n-r)!r!(n-r-1)!}$

Cancelling like factors gives

$n(n-1)!/r!(n-r)! = C(n,r)$

14. a) $C(r + c - 2, r - 1)$

b) The proof is by induction on $r + c$, that is, by diagonals. Step 1, $r + c = 3$, is verified by inspection. Step 2: Divide the portion of the triangle from the upper left corner to the entry d at row r and column c into regions as shown:

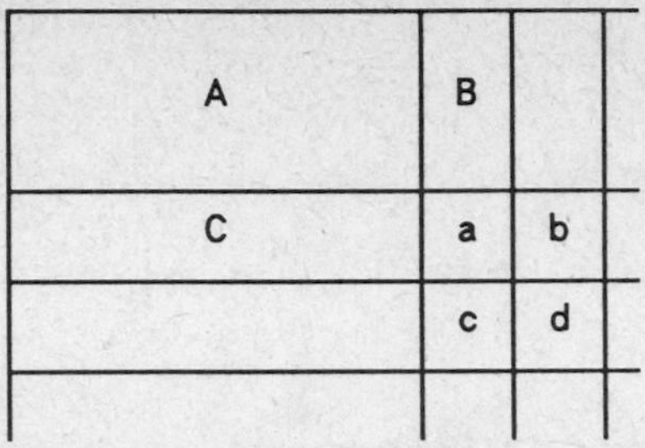

A	B		
C	a	b	
	c	d	

where each capital letter represents the sum of the entries in the region. By the induction hypothesis, $a = A + 1$, $b = A + B + 1$, and $c = A + C + 1$. Therefore

$$\begin{aligned} d = b + c &= A + B + 1 + A + C + 1 \\ &= a - 1 + B + 1 + A + C + 1 \\ &= A + B + C + a - 1 \end{aligned}$$

15. a)
$$nC(n-1,r-1)/r = \frac{(n-1)!}{r(r-1)!(n-1-r+1)!} = \frac{n!}{r!(n-r)!}$$
$$= C(n,r)$$

b) The intermediate result after the k-th division is

$$\frac{(n-r+1)(n-r+2)\ \dots\ (n-r+k)}{1 \times 2 \times \dots \times k} = C(n-r+k,k)$$

Section 6.4

1. a) $x^6 + 6x^5 + 15x^4 + 20x^3 + 15x^2 + 6x + 1$

   b) $625 - 1000a + 600a^2 - 160a^3 + 16a^4$

2. 35   3. 1540

4. a) $2002x^5y^9$ b) $220x^3$

5. $-10500000x^3$ 6. $90720x^4y^4$

7. Step 1: If $n = 1$, $C(1,0) + C(1,1) = 1 + 1 = 2^1$.

Step 2:

$$\sum_{r=0}^{n+1} C(n+1,r) = C(n+1,0) + \sum_{r=1}^{n} [C(n,r) + C(n,r-1)] + C(n+1,n+1)$$

$$= \sum_{r=0}^{n} C(n,r) + \sum_{r=1}^{n+1} C(n,r-1)$$

$$= 2^{n-1} + 2^{n-1} = 2^n$$

8. $C(n + 1,r + 1)$

$= C(n,r) + C(n,r + 1)$

$= C(n,r) + C(n - 1,r) + C(n - 1,r + 1)$

$= C(n,r) + C(n - 1,r) + C(n - 2,r) + C(n - 2,r + 1)$

$= \ldots$

$$= C(n,r) + \ldots + C(n - (n - r),r) + \underbrace{C(n - (n - r),r + 1)}_{= 0}$$

9. Choose $r = 2$.

10. Let X be a set of 2n elements, and let $X = A \cup B$ where A and B have n elements. An n-element subset of X may have r elements in A and n-r elements in B. Given r, there are $C(n,r)$ ways to choose the subset of A and $C(n,n-r) = C(n,r)$ ways to choose the subset of B. So the total number of subsets of X is the sum of the products of these.

11. This is the binomial expansion of $(1 - 1)^n$.

12. 2^{n-1} even, same number odd.

13. $$C(n,r+1) = \frac{n!}{(r+1)![n-(r+1)]!} = \frac{n!}{(r+1)!(n-r-1)!}$$

$$\frac{n-r}{r+1} C(n,r) = \frac{(n-r)n!}{(r+1)r!(n-r)!} = \frac{(n-r)n!}{(r+1)r!(n-r)(n-r-1)!}$$

$$= \frac{n!}{(r+1)r!(n-r-1)!} = \frac{n!}{(r+1)!(n-r-1)!}$$

$$= C(n,r+1)$$

14. This is the binomial expansion of $(2 + 1)^n$.

15.

$$C(n,r)C(r,k) = \frac{n!}{r!(n-r)!} \times \frac{r!}{k!(r-k)!}$$

$$= \frac{n!r!}{r!k!(n-r)!(r-k)!} = \frac{n!}{k!(n-r)!(r-k)!}$$

$$C(n,k)C(n-k,r-k) = \frac{n!}{k!(n-k)!} \times \frac{(n-k)!}{(r-k)!(n-k-r+k)!}$$

$$= \frac{n!(n-k)!}{k!(n-k)!(r-k)!(n-r)!}$$

$$= \frac{n!}{k!(r-k)!(n-r)!}$$

$$= C(n,r)C(r,k)$$

16. Let X be a set of m + n elements, and let X = A U B where A has m elements and B has n elements. An r-element subset of X may have r-k elements in A and k elements in B. Given k, there are C(m,r-k) ways to choose the subset of A and C(n,k) ways to choose the subset of B. So the total number of subsets of X is the sum of the products of these.

Section 6.5

1. { rr, rg, ry, gr, gy, yy }
2. A = { 2, 4, 6, 8, 10, 12 }
3. p_1 and p_5
4. a) 0.07 b) 0.68 c) 0.69 d) 0.32

5. 1/2   6. 1/2   7. 13(48)/C(52,5) = 0.00024

8. a) 6.299×10^{-12} b) 0.00882   c) 0.01279

9. 7/32   10. 219/256   11. 4/9   12. 1/8   13. 0.431

14. a) 0.00163   b) 8/9   15. $30/9^4 = 0.0046$

16. 1.2043×10^{-10} 17. 7/9   18. 0   19. $1/(5!)^4$

20. a) 1/3   b) 25.33

c) Since the number of persons expected to guess correctly is 25, you may guess that the probability that 34 or more will guess correctly is quite small. (In fact, it

is $\sum_{n=34}^{76} C(76,n)(2/3)^{76-n}(1/3)^n = 0.017$)

The result is not likely to be the result of chance.

21. 7/64

22. a) 0.4389   b) 0.4221   c) 0.5610

23. a) 0.001441   b) 0.00198   c) 0.003940

d) 0.000015   e) 0.095078   f) 0.422569

24. $p(A \cup B) = \sum_{x \in A \cup B} p(x) = \sum_{x \in A} p(x) + \sum_{x \in B} p(x) - \sum_{x \in A \cap B} p(x)$

$= p(A) + p(B) - p(A \cap B)$

Section 6.6

1.

outcome	probability
both successful	0.0814
X successful only	0.2886
Y successful only	0.1386
neither successful	0.4914

2.

Akron	Auckland	Ahmedabad	Probability
rain	rain	rain	0.064125
rain	rain	dry	0.003375
rain	dry	rain	0.078375
rain	dry	dry	0.004125
dry	rain	rain	0.363375
dry	rain	dry	0.019125
dry	dry	rain	0.444125
dry	dry	dry	0.023375

3.

outcome	probability
0	0.2215
1	0.4114
2	0.2743
3	0.0815
4	0.0107
5	0.0005

4. yes 5. yes

6. $1 - (0.62)^{20} = .99993$ 7. 12.5

8. a) 0.0025 b) 0.095 c) 0.9025

9. $20(1/36)(35/36)^{19} \approx 0.3253$

10. a) 3/13 b) 1/2 c) 1/2

11. a) 13/19 b) 13/20

12. a) 0.5876 b) 0.5556 c) 0.0076

13. From the tree diagram, the probability that both are defective is the product (2/14)(1/13) = 0.011. The probability that neither is defective is (12/14)(11/13) = 0.725.

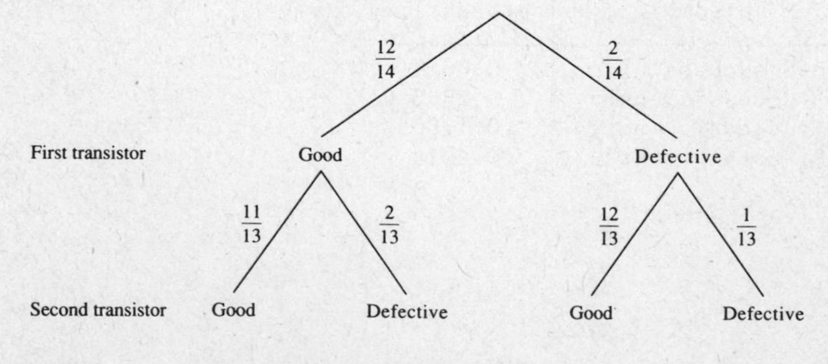

14. 66/90 15. 1/15 16. 1/7

17. $0.000636 = C(13,5) / [C(52,5) - C(39,5)]$

18. 7 19. 15 cents 20. -1 dollar

21. -20 points 22. -84 cents 23. 12.6 seconds

24. 150.75 milliseconds 25. 1

26. a) Since $A \subset B$, $A \cap B = A$ so that

$$p(A|B) = p(A \cap B)/p(B) = p(A)/p(B)$$

b) Since $B \subset A$, $A \cap B = A$ so that

$$p(A|B) = p(A \cap B)/p(B) = p(B)/p(B) = 1$$

Chapter Review

1. a) 3024 b) 126 2. 720 3. 40,320; 9,979,200

4. 66 5. 30 6. 60

7. a) 1,293,600 b) 48/203 c) 60/229

8. a) 1024 b) 176/1024

9. 1287 10. 65,780 11. 128 12. 12 13. 2

14. 7,893,600; 303,600 15. $(9!/2!)/2 = 90,720$ 16. 32

17. a) $x^7+28x^6+336x^5+2240x^4+8960x^3+21504x^2+28672x+16384$

b) $27 - 18a + 12a^2 - 8a^3$

18. $C(64,20)$ 19. $9,496,093,750x^9$

20.
$$C(n+1,r) = \frac{(n+1)!}{r!(n+1-r)!}$$

$$C(n,r-1) + C(n,r) = \frac{n!}{(r-1)!(n-r+1)!} + \frac{n!}{r!(n-r)!}$$

$$= \frac{n!r!(n-r)! + n!(r-1)!(n-r+1)!}{(r-1)!(n-r+1)!r!(n-r)!}$$

$$= \frac{n!(r-1)!(n-r)![r + (n-r+1)]}{(r-1)!(n-r+1)!r!(n-r)!}$$

$$= \frac{n!(n+1)}{r!(n-r+1)!} = \frac{(n+1)!}{r!(n+1-r)!}$$

$$= C(n+1,r)$$

21.

$$C(2n,2) = \frac{(2n)!}{2!(2n - 2)!} = \frac{(2n)(2n-1)(2n-2)!}{2!(2n - 2)!}$$

$$= \frac{(2n)(2n - 1)}{2!} = 2n^2 - n$$

$$2C(n,2) + n^2 = \frac{2n!}{2!(n - 2)!} + n^2 = \frac{n(n-1)(n-2)!}{(n - 2)!} + n^2$$

$$= n(n - 1) + n^2 = 2n^2 - n$$

$$= C(2n,2)$$

22.

$$rC(n,r) = \frac{rn!}{r!(n - r)!} = \frac{n!}{(r-1)!(n-r)!}$$

$$nC(n-1,r-1) = \frac{n(n - 1)!}{(r-1)!(n-1-r+1)!} = \frac{n!}{(r-1)!(n-r)!}$$

$$= rC(n,r)$$

23. $C(2n+2,n+1) = C(2n+1,n) + C(2n+1,n+1)$

$$= [C(2n,n-1) + C(2n,n)] + [C(2n,n) + C(2n,n+1)]$$

24. A product of k consecutive integers ending in $n + k$ is the numerator of $C(n + k,k)$.

25. a) 7 b) 16,807 c) 0.000416

26. a) 156 b) $(156)^5$ c) $1/(156)^4$

27. 48/(48 + C(4,3)C(48,2)) = 1/95

28. 1/5 29. 91/6 30. 0.8174

Chapter 7

Section 7.1

1.

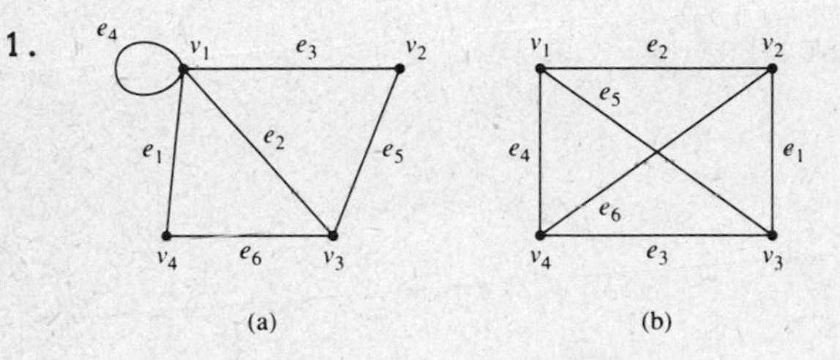

2. a)

	v_1	v_2	v_3	v_4	v_5
e_1	1	1	0	0	0
e_2	0	1	1	0	0
e_3	0	1	0	1	0
e_4	1	0	0	1	0
e_5	0	0	1	1	0
e_6	0	0	0	1	1

b)

	v_1	v_2	v_3	v_4	v_5	v_6
e_1	1	0	0	0	0	0
e_2	0	1	0	0	0	0
e_3	0	0	1	0	0	0
e_4	0	0	0	1	0	0
e_5	0	0	0	0	1	1

c)

	v_1	v_2	v_3	v_4
e_1	1	1	0	0
e_2	1	1	0	0
e_3	1	0	1	0
e_4	1	0	1	0
e_5	1	0	1	0
e_6	1	0	0	1
e_7	1	0	0	1

3. e_1 is incident to v_1 in graphs a and c

e_1 is incident to v_2 in graphs b and c

v_1 and v_2 are adjacent in graphs b and c

4. a

5. Degree 2: Grand Isle, Essex, and Windham

Degree 3: Rutland and Bennington

Degree 4: Franklin, Orleans, and Orange

Degree 5: all other counties

6. a) Vertices of set V_1 have degrees 2, 2, and 1 (from top to bottom.) Vertices of set V_2 have degrees 1, 1, 2, and 1.

   b) Vertices of set V_1 have degrees 1, 3, and 1. Vertices of set V_2 have degrees 1, 1, 0, 2, 0.

   c) Vertices of set V_1 have degrees 2, 3, and 3. Vertices of set V_2 have degrees 2, 3, and 3.

7. a and b

8. 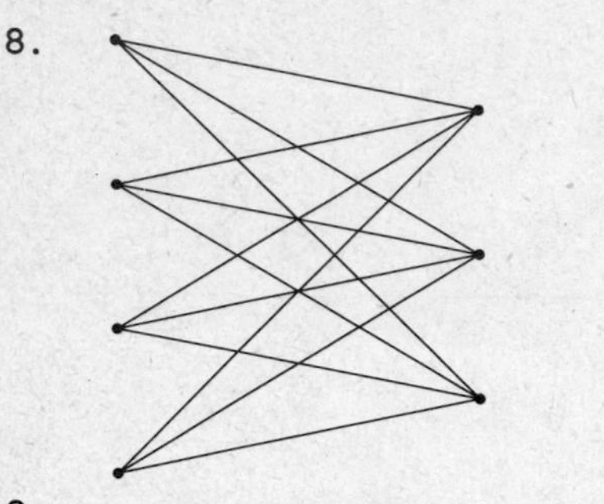

9. 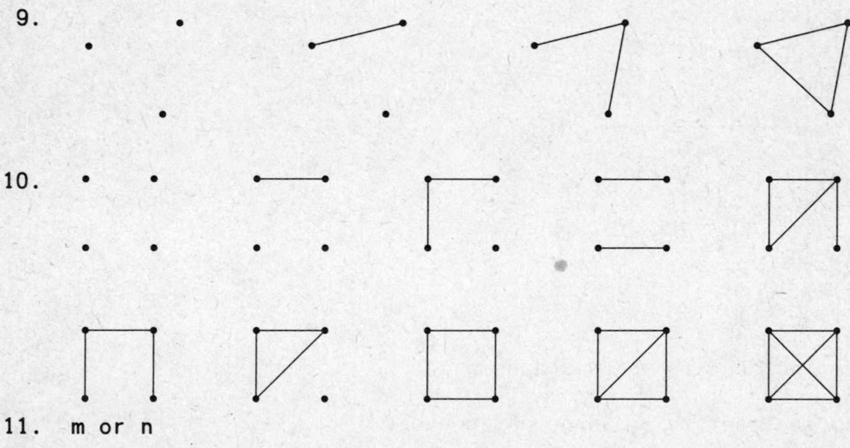

10.

11. m or n

12. m + n; mn

13.

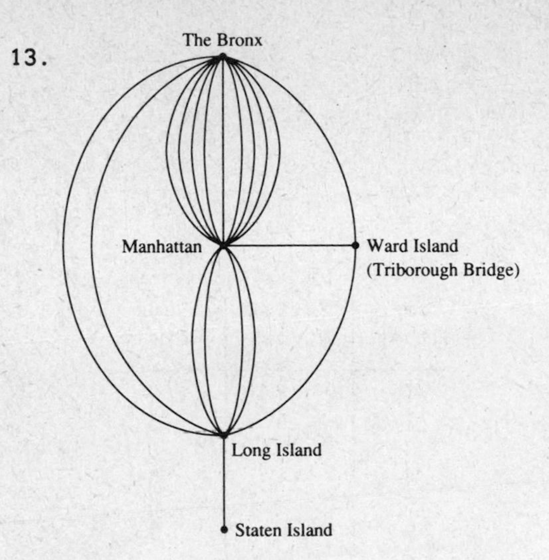

14.

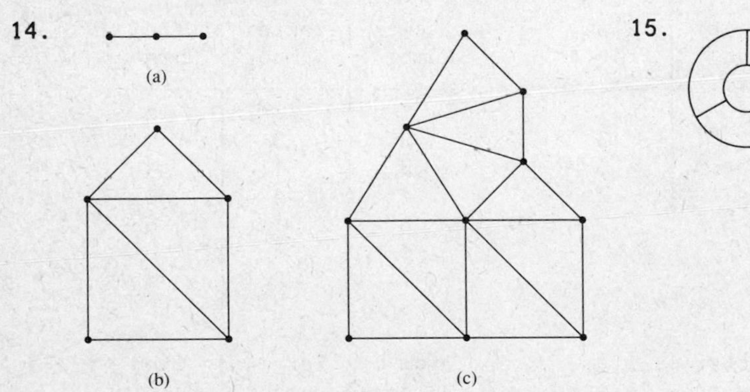

15.

16. a)

	v_1	v_2	v_3	v_4
v_1	0	0	1	0
v_2	–	0	1	1
v_3	–	–	0	0
v_4	–	–	–	0

b)

	v_1	v_2	v_3	v_4
v_1	0	1	1	0
v_2	–	0	0	1
v_3	–	–	0	1
v_4	–	–	–	0

c)

	v_1	v_2	v_3	v_4	v_5
v_1	0	2	0	0	0
v_2	–	0	0	0	0
v_3	–	–	0	1	0
v_4	–	–	–	0	1
v_5	–	–	–	–	0

17.

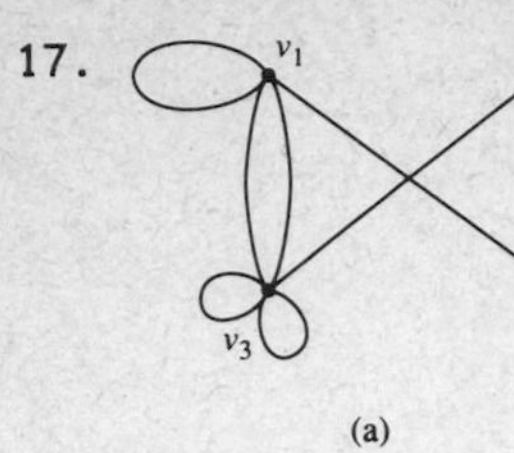

(a)

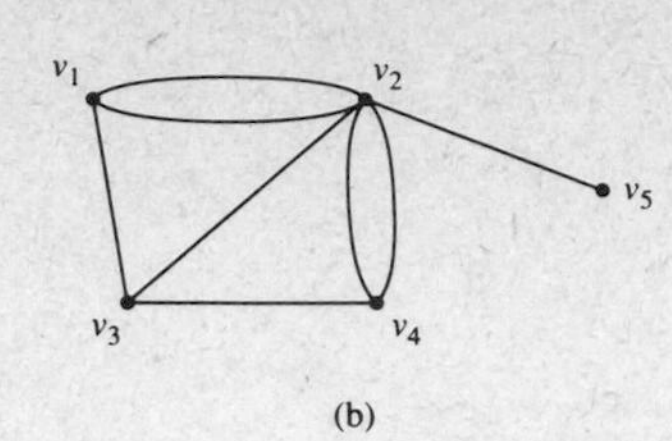

(b)

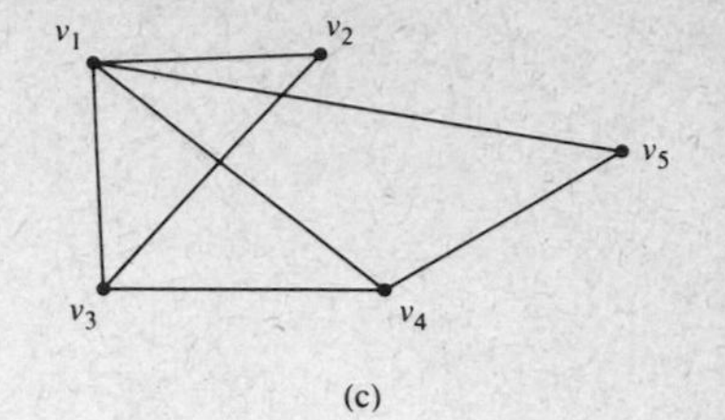

(c)

18. a)

Vertex Number	Item Pointer
1	1
2	2
3	4
4	6

Item Number	Vertex Number	Item Pointer
1	3	0
2	3	3
3	4	0
4	1	5
5	2	0
6	2	0

b)

Vertex Number	Item Pointer
1	1
2	3
3	5
4	7

Item Number	Vertex Number	Item Pointer
1	2	2
2	3	0
3	1	4
4	4	0
5	1	6
6	4	0
7	2	8
8	3	0

19.

Vertex Number	Item Pointer
1	1
2	3
3	6
4	8
5	12

Item Number	Vertex Number	Item Pointer
1	4	2
2	2	0
3	1	4
4	4	5
5	3	0
6	2	7
7	4	0
8	1	9
9	2	10
10	3	11
11	5	0
12	4	0

20.

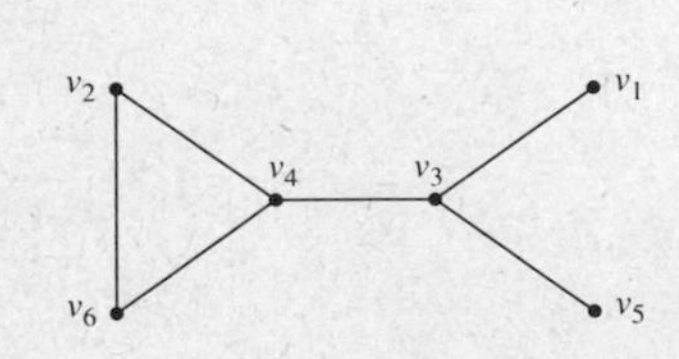

21.

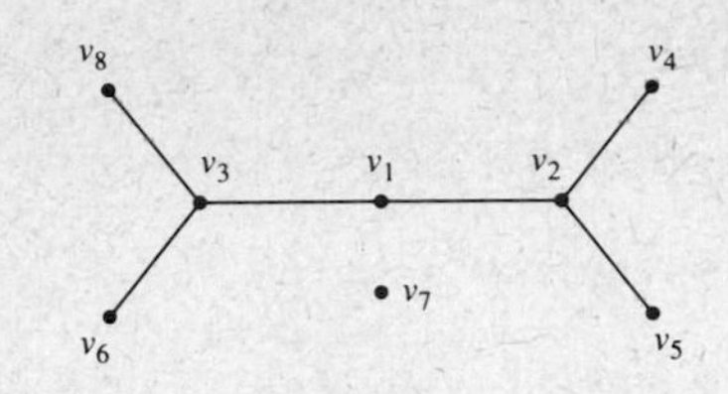

22. Each entry above the main diagonal is 1. All other entries are 0.

23. It has an m x n rectangle of 1's in the upper right corner; all other entries are zero.

24. Iceland, 0; U.S., 4. Under international law, the border of a country lies 3 miles off its coastline. The U.S. has one border with Mexico, two with Canada, and one with the U.S.S.R (in the Bering Strait).

Section 7.2

1.

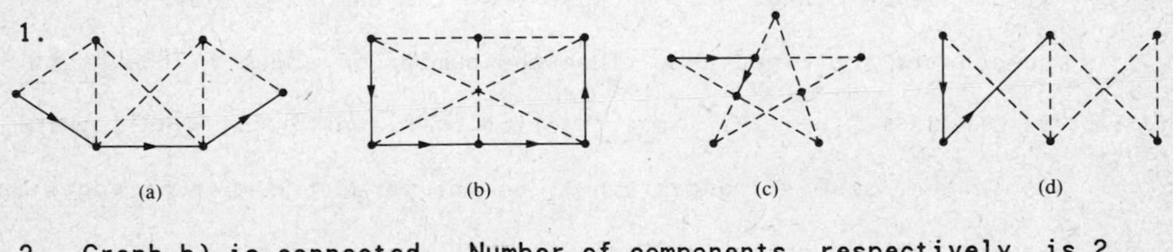

(a) (b) (c) (d)

2. Graph b) is connected. Number of components, respectively, is 2, 1, 9, and 3.

3.

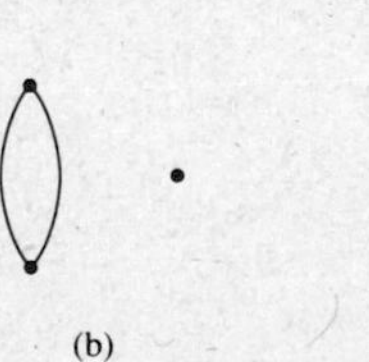

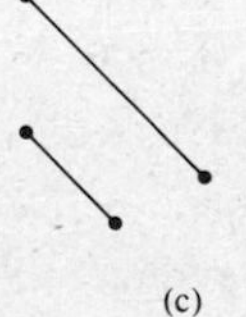

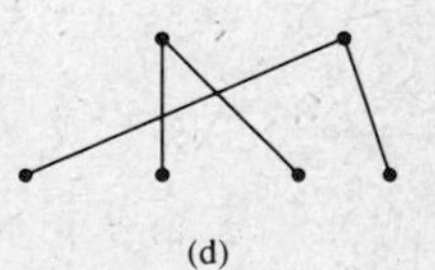

(a) (b) (c) (d)

4. a, c, and d

Start

(a)

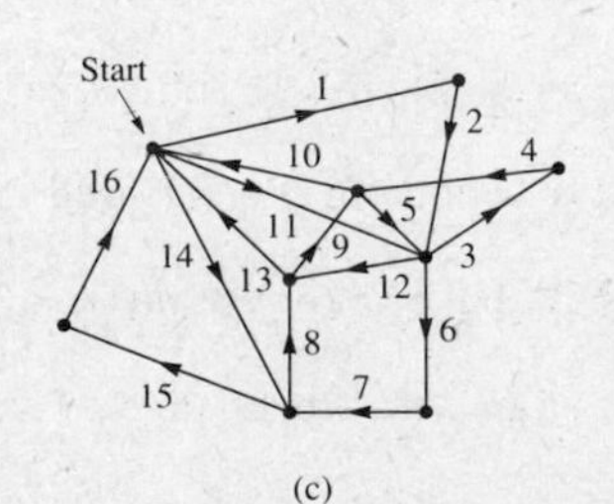

(c)

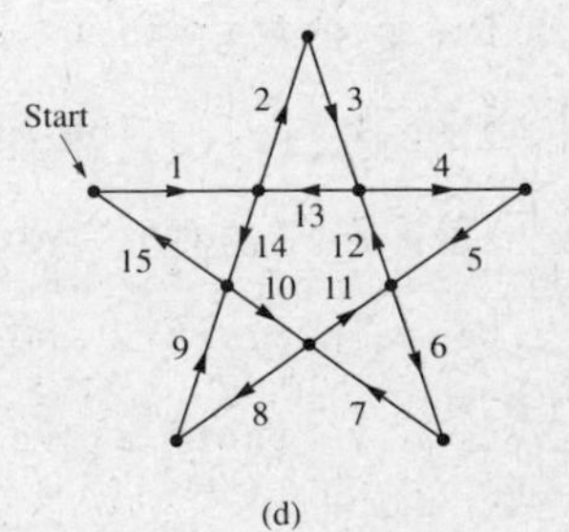

(d)

5. R is reflexive since for each vertex v, there is the trivial path (of length 0) from v to v. R is symmetric since if there is a path from u to v, then there is a path from v to u. R is transitive since a path from u to v can be combined with a path from v to w to form a path from u to w.

6. Let H be a non-connected simple graph with n vertices and the largest possible number of edges. Then H must have two components, because otherwise you could add an edge connecting two of the components and the graph would still not be connected. Each of the components must be complete, because otherwise you could add an edge to a non-complete component and the graph would still not be connected. Suppose that the number of edges in the components are k and n-k. Then the number of edges in the graph is C(k,2) + C(n-k,2). As a function of k over $1 \leq k \leq n-1$, this is largest at k = 1 and k = n-1; so the largest number of edges in a nonconnected graph is C(n-1,2).

7. No. If G consists of a connected graph H with an Euler circuit and one or more isolated vertices, then the Euler circuit for H is also an Euler circuit for G.

8. For odd values of n

9. m and n must both be even.

10. No. Staten Island has degree 1.

11. The proof is by induction on the number of edges in the walk.
Step 1: n=1. The walk is a loop, which is a cycle.
Step 2: Assume that all closed walks of odd length less than n contain cycles, and let W be a closed walk of odd length n. If W is not itself a cycle, then two vertices of the walk are equal.

The common vertex divides W into two closed walks, one of which must be of odd length and so contains a cycle.

Section 7.3

1.

	edges	vertices	faces	Euler's formula
a)	3	2	3	2 - 3 + 3 = 2
b)	5	5	2	5 - 5 + 2 = 2
c)	9	10	1	10 - 9 + 1 = 2
d)	17	12	7	12 - 17 + 7 = 2
e)	9	5	6	5 - 9 + 6 = 2
f)	3	2	3	2 - 3 + 3 = 2
g)	3	1	4	1 - 3 + 4 = 2
h)	0	1	1	1 - 0 + 1 = 2

2.

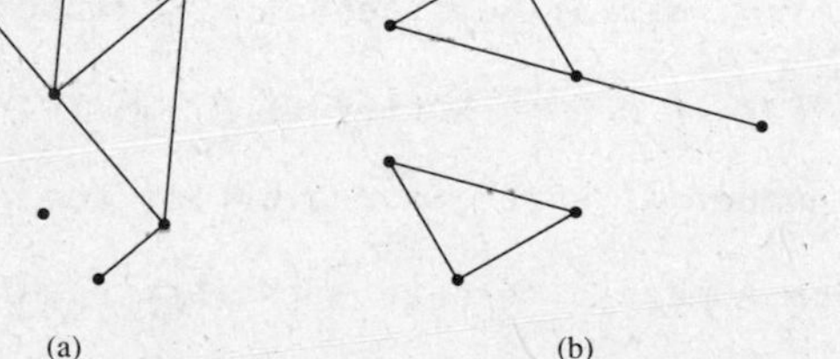

3. Suppose H_1 has p_1 vertices, q_1 edges, and r_1 faces, and H_2 has p_2 vertices, q_2 edges, and r_2 faces, where $p_1 + p_2 = p$, $q_1 + q_2 + 1 = q$, and $r_1 + r_2 - 1 = r$. Since r_1 equals the number of inside faces + 1 (the outside face), r_2 equals the number of inside faces + 1; r equals the number of faces inside H_1 + the number inside H_2 + 1, which is $r_1 + r_2 - 1$. So

$$\begin{aligned} p - q + r &= p_1 + p_2 - q_1 - q_2 - 1 + r_1 + r_2 - 1 \\ &= (p_1 - q_1 + r_1) + (p_2 - q_2 + r_2) - 2 \\ &= 2 + 2 - 2 \\ &= 2 \end{aligned}$$

4. The chosen edge e_0 and the shortest path connecting its ends need not enclose a face; it may loop around the torus instead.

5. Each face must be bounded by at least four edges, and each edge

has two sides. Therefore 4r is at most the number of face boundaries, which is 2q.

6. If $K_{3,3}$ is planar, Euler's Theorem says that an embedding of $K_{3,3}$ must have 5 faces. Exercise 5 then says that $4(5) \leq 2(9)$ which is wrong.

7.

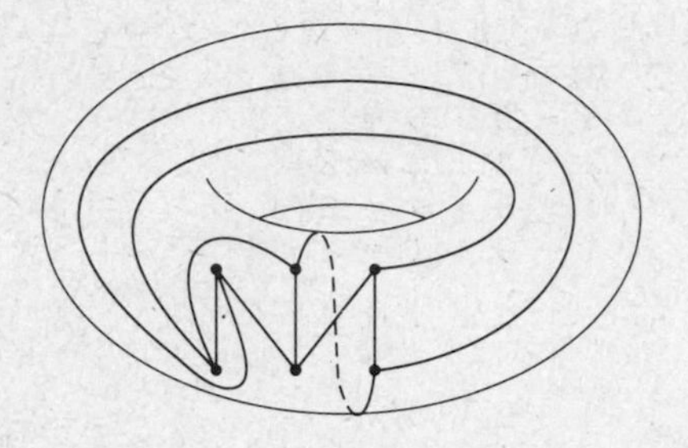

8. Let A and B be the two sets of vertices of $K_{m,n}$ such that every edge connects a vertex of A to a vertex of B. Any cycle in $K_{m,n}$ must have an even number of edges; moreover, as you traverse the cycle, vertices from A must alternate with vertices from B. Therefore, the number of A vertices in the cycle equals the number of B vertices. If the cycle includes all vertices, m = n.

9.

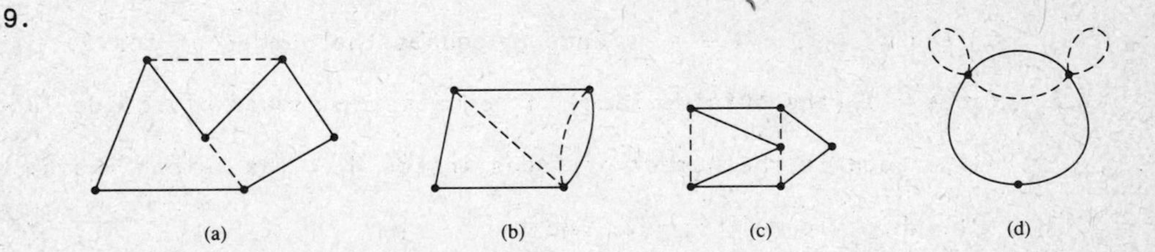

(a) (b) (c) (d)

10.

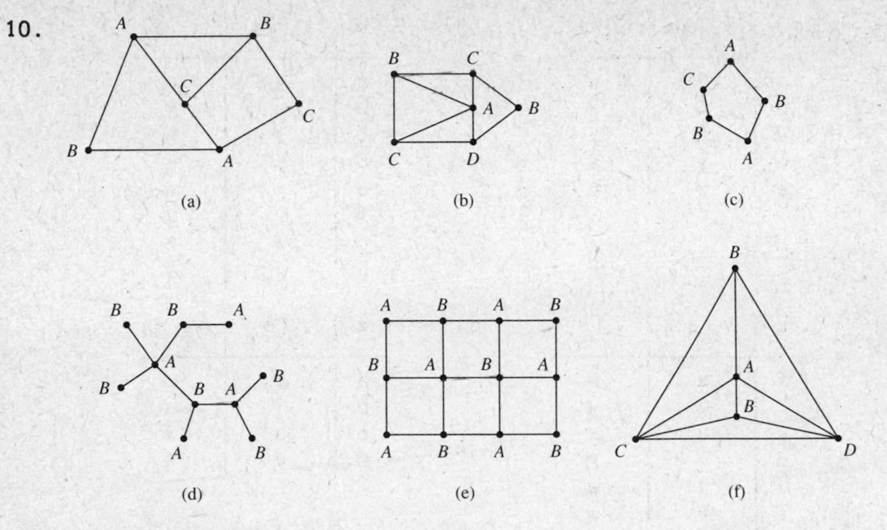

(a) (b) (c) (d) (e) (f)

11. Proof by induction on the number of circles. Step 1: trivial for one circle. Step 2: when adding a new circle, reverse all colors inside the new circle.

12.

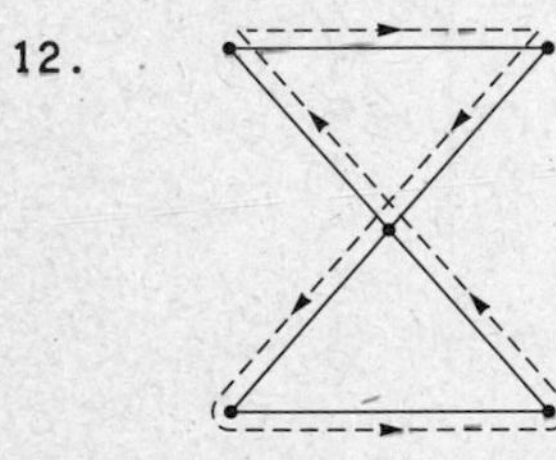

13.

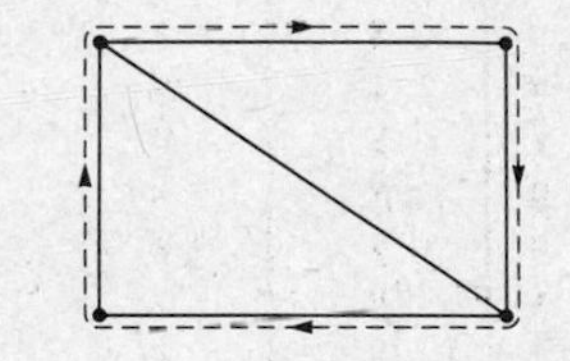

Section 7.4

1.

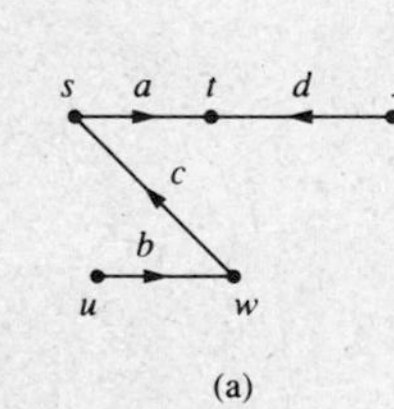

(a)

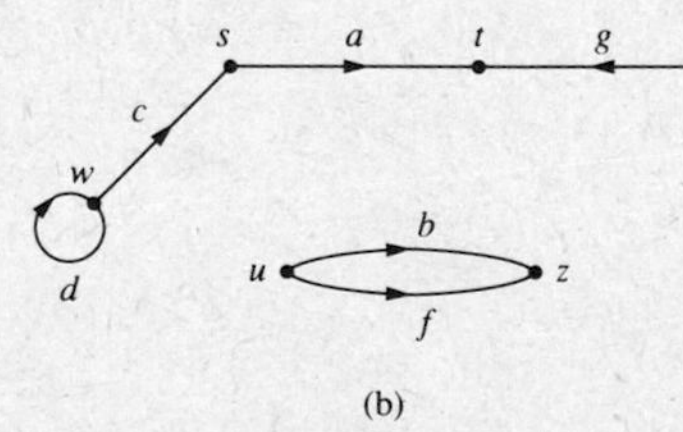

(b)

2.

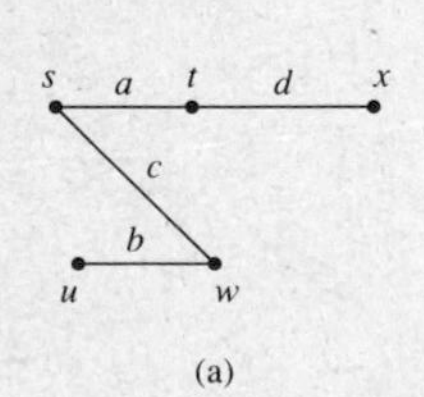

(a)

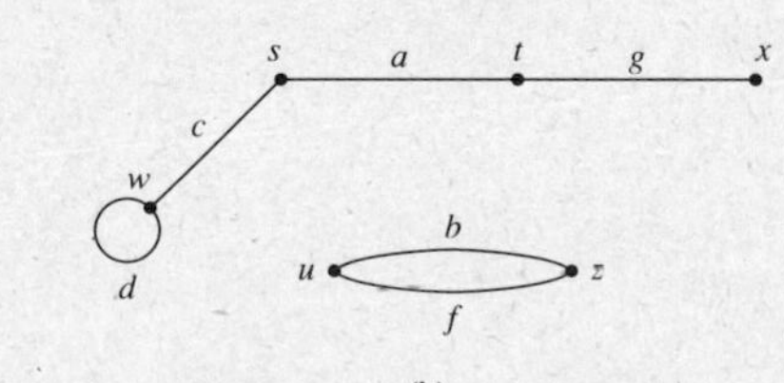

(b)

3. a)

e	$v_s(e)$	$v_e(e)$
a	v	w
b	w	x
c	x	y
d	y	z
e	z	u

b)

e	$v_s(e)$	$v_e(e)$
a	y	u
b	u	v
c	v	w
d	u	w
e	y	w
f	y	x
g	w	x
h	v	x

c)

e	$v_s(e)$	$v_e(e)$
a	u	w
b	u	v
c	u	x
d	v	x
e	x	w
f	v	w

d)

e	$v_s(e)$	$v_e(e)$
a	z	u
b	y	u
c	u	x
d	v	x

e)

e	$v_s(e)$	$v_e(e)$
a	u	v
b	v	w
c	w	x
d	x	z
e	z	u
f	y	u
g	y	v
h	y	w
i	y	x
j	y	z

f)

e	$v_s(e)$	$v_e(e)$
a	y	u
b	u	y
c	u	v
d	v	v
e	v	w
f	w	x
g	x	w
h	x	y

4. a, b, c, d, and e

5.

	vertex	indegree	outdegree
a)	u	1	0
	v	0	1
	w	1	1
	x	1	1
	y	1	1
	z	1	1
b)	u	1	2
	v	1	2
	w	3	1
	x	2	1
	y	1	2
c)	u	0	3
	v	1	2
	w	3	0
	x	2	1
d)	u	2	1
	v	0	1
	w	0	0
	x	2	0
	y	0	1
	z	0	1
e)	u	2	1
	v	2	1
	w	2	1
	x	2	1
	y	0	5
	z	2	1
f)	u	1	2
	v	3	1
	w	1	2
	x	1	2
	y	2	1

6. b

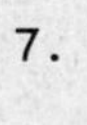

7.

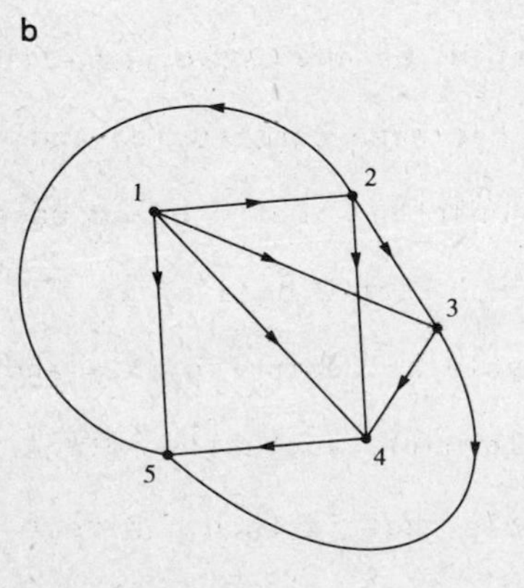

8.

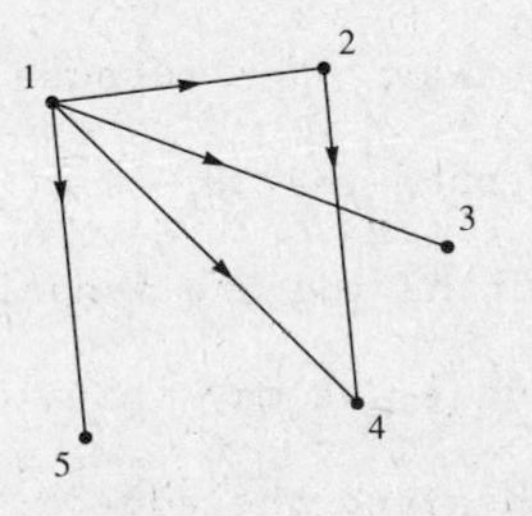

9.

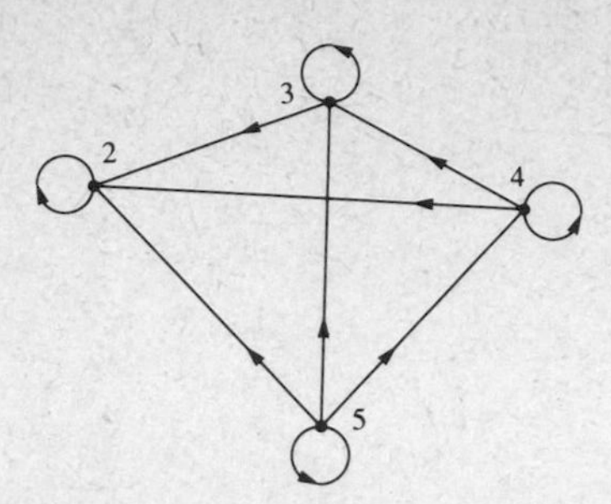

10. a, c

11. Each edge contributes 1 to the outdegree of its start vertex, so the sum of outdegrees is equal to the number of edges. Similar for indegrees.

12. Only when the equivalence relation is the empty relation on the empty set.

13. 14. a, d

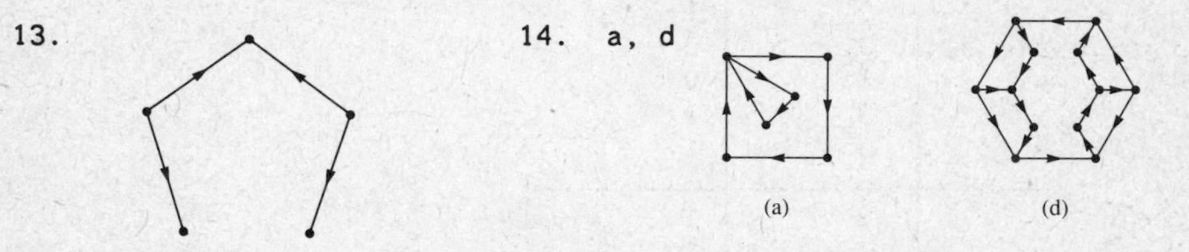

15. Let G be a connected graph without bridges, and let e be an edge of G. Remove e from G leaving H. H is connected, so there is a path in H connecting the ends of e. This path, together with e, forms a cycle containing e. Again let G be a connected graph without bridges; we will construct a sequence H_1, ..., H_n of successively larger subgraphs of G, each of which is strongly connected, and such that H_n = G. Let H_1 be any cycle and direct it either way. Now suppose that H_k has been constructed and directed such that H_k is strongly connected. Let e be an edge not in H_k, but having one endpoint a in H_k. Let C be a cycle containing e. We may think of the cycle as beginning at a and leaving H along the edge e; the cycle must eventually return to H. Let b be the first vertex of the cycle that is in H. Direct the

edges from a to b along the cycle in the direction that we just traveled from a to b, and add these edges to H_k. The result is a larger subgraph H_{k+1} which is also strongly connected.

16. Refer to the proof of Theorem 7.6. If a directed Euler circuit exists, it contributes 1 to the indegree and 1 to the outdegree of every vertex through which it passes; this shows that indegree = outdegree at each vertex. Conversely, if indegree = outdegree at each vertex, the construction in the second part of the proof may be carried out by choosing an unused outbound edge at each step; because, if there are any unused edges, there are unused outbound edges because the number of unused outbound edges is equal to the number of unused inbound edges.

17. a and c

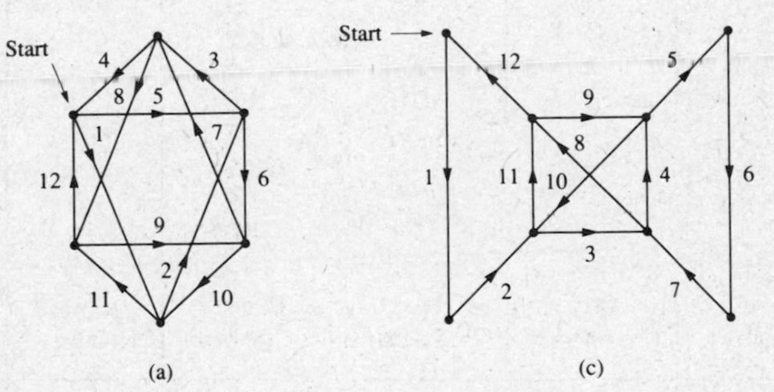

18. Counterexample: let X = { a, b } and let R = { (a,a), (b,b) }.

19. Counterexample: let X = { a, b } and let R = { (a,a), (b,b), (a,b) }. Then R is a total order but there is no directed path from b to a.

20. a)

	u	v	w	x	y	z
u	0	0	0	0	0	0
v	0	0	1	0	0	0
w	0	0	0	1	0	0
x	0	0	0	0	1	0
y	0	0	0	0	0	1
z	1	0	0	0	0	0

b)

	u	v	w	x	y
u	0	1	1	0	0
v	0	0	1	1	0
w	0	0	0	1	0
x	0	0	0	0	1
y	1	0	1	0	0

c)

	u	v	w	x
u	0	1	1	1
v	0	0	1	1
w	0	0	0	0
x	0	0	1	0

d)

	u	v	w	x	y	z
u	0	0	0	1	0	0
v	0	0	0	1	0	0
w	0	0	0	0	0	0
x	0	0	0	0	0	0
y	1	0	0	0	0	0
z	1	0	0	0	0	0

e)

	u	v	w	x	y	z
u	0	1	0	0	0	0
v	0	0	1	0	0	0
w	0	0	0	1	0	0
x	0	0	0	0	0	1
y	1	1	1	1	0	1
z	1	0	0	0	0	0

f)

	u	v	w	x	y
u	0	1	0	0	1
v	0	1	0	0	0
w	0	1	0	1	0
x	0	0	1	0	1
y	1	0	0	0	0

21. a)

Vertex Number	Out Pointer	In Pointer
1 (v)	1	0
2 (w)	3	2
3 (x)	5	4
4 (y)	7	6
5 (z)	9	8
6 (u)	0	10

Item Number	Vertex Number	Item Pointer
1	2	0
2	1	0
3	3	0
4	2	0
5	4	0
6	3	0
7	5	0
8	4	0
9	6	0
10	5	0

b)

Vertex Number	Out Pointer	In Pointer
1 (u)	2	1
2 (v)	5	4
3 (w)	10	7
4 (x)	13	11
5 (y)	15	14

Item Number	Vertex Number	Item Pointer
1	5	0
2	2	3
3	3	0
4	1	0
5	3	6
6	4	0
7	1	8
8	2	9
9	5	0
10	4	0
11	2	12
12	3	0
13	5	0
14	4	0
15	1	16
16	3	0

22.

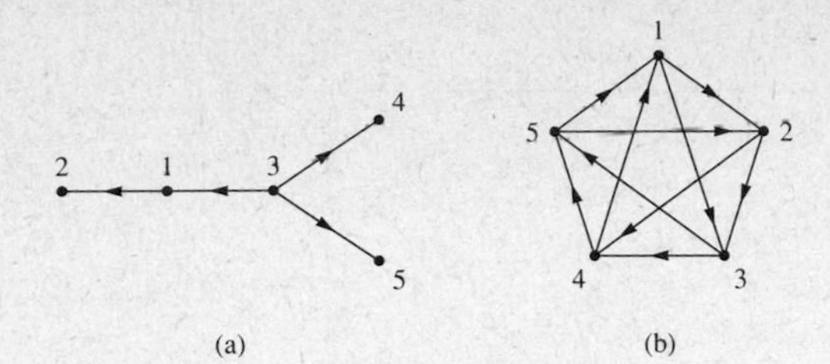

23. a) Outdegree(v) b) Indegree(v)

Section 7.5

1.

Step	Sel.	a	b	c	d	e	f
1	c	∞	7	0	7	5	2
2	f	6	4	0	7	5	2
3	b	5	4	0	7	5	2
4	a	5	4	0	7	5	2
5	e	5	4	0	6	5	2
6	d	5	4	0	6	5	2

2.

Step	Sel.	a	b	c	d	e	f
1	d	∞	∞	7	0	1	∞
2	e	∞	∞	6	0	1	14
3	c	∞	13	6	0	1	8
4	f	12	10	6	0	1	8
5	b	11	10	6	0	1	8
6	a	11	10	6	0	1	8

3.

Step	Sel.	a	b	c	d	e	f	g	h	z
1	a	0	1	∞	2	∞	∞	∞	∞	∞
2	b	0	1	7	2	6	∞	∞	∞	∞
3	d	0	1	7	2	3	∞	7	∞	∞
4	e	0	1	7	2	3	10	6	11	∞
5	g	0	1	7	2	3	10	6	10	∞
6	c	0	1	7	2	3	9	6	10	∞
7	f	0	1	7	2	3	9	6	10	11
8	h	0	1	7	2	3	9	6	10	11
9	z	0	1	7	2	3	9	6	10	11
	Pred.	–	a	b	a	d	c	e	g	f

4.

Step	Sel.	a	b	c	d	e	f	g	h	z
1	z	∞	∞	∞	∞	∞	2	∞	5	0
2	f	∞	∞	4	∞	9	2	∞	4	0
3	c	∞	10	4	∞	9	2	∞	4	0
4	h	∞	10	4	∞	9	2	8	4	0
5	g	∞	10	4	13	9	2	8	4	0
6	e	∞	10	4	10	9	2	8	4	0
7	b	11	10	4	10	9	2	8	4	0
8	d	11	10	4	10	9	2	8	4	0
9	a	11	10	4	10	9	2	8	4	0
	Pred.	b	c	f	e	f	z	e	f	-

5. adeg 6. zfhg

7. The algorithm terminates after processing all vertices in the same connected component as the starting vertex.

8. Stop when Dijkstra's algorithm selects the target vertex.

9. No; consider a triangle with edge weights of 1, 2, and 3.

10. Interpret w(i,j) as the weight of the edge directed from v_i to v_j (this may be different from w(j,i)). No modification to the algorithm is required.

11. Yes; but first discard all loops, and where there are multiple edges, discard all but the shortest.

12. We used the fact that when an edge is added to a path, the new path has a greater length.

Chapter Review

1.

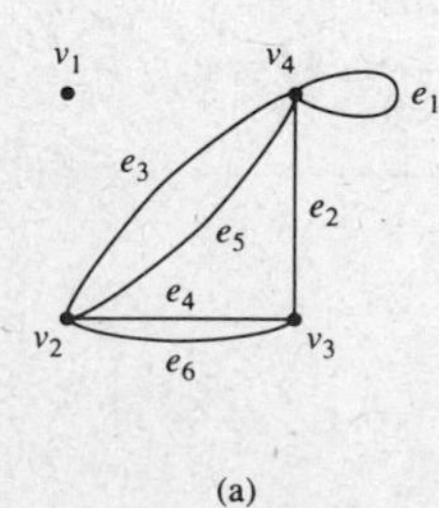

(a)

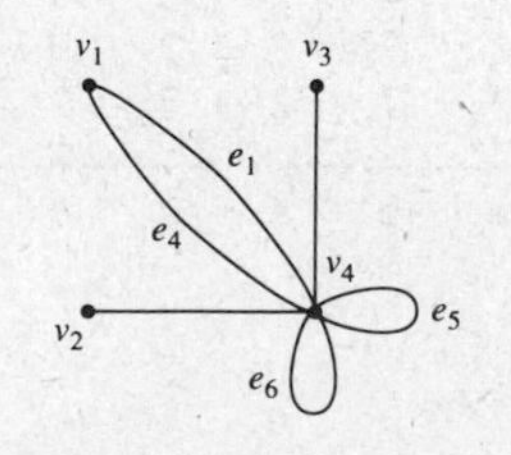

(b)

2. a)

	v_1	v_2	v_3	v_4	v_5	v_6	v_7	v_8	v_9
e_1	1	1	0	0	0	0	0	0	0
e_2	0	1	1	0	0	0	0	0	0
e_3	0	0	1	1	0	0	0	0	0
e_4	1	0	0	1	0	0	0	0	0
e_5	0	1	0	0	1	0	0	0	0
e_6	0	0	0	0	1	1	0	0	0
e_7	0	0	0	0	0	1	1	0	0
e_8	0	0	0	0	0	0	1	1	0
e_9	0	0	1	0	0	0	0	1	0
e_{10}	0	0	1	0	0	0	0	0	1
e_{11}	0	1	0	0	0	0	0	0	1
e_{12}	0	0	0	0	0	1	0	0	1
e_{13}	0	0	0	0	0	1	0	0	0
e_{14}	0	0	0	0	0	1	0	1	0
e_{15}	0	0	0	0	0	0	0	1	1

b)

	v	w	x
f	1	1	0
g	1	0	1
h	0	1	1
j	0	0	1
k	0	1	1

3.

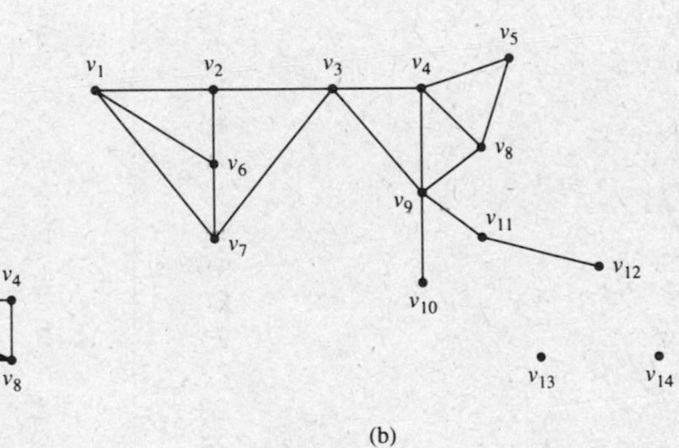

(a) (b)

4. Refer to the figure given above for exercise 3 for the vertex numbering used in these answers.

a) 3, 5, 3, 2, 2, 4, 3, 4

b) 3, 3, 4, 4, 2, 3, 3, 3, 5, 1, 2, 1, 0, 0

5.

	v_1	v_2	v_3	v_4	v_5	v_6	v_7	v_8
v_1	0	1	0	0	1	1	0	0
v_2	–	0	1	0	0	1	1	1
v_3	–	–	0	1	0	0	0	1
v_4	–	–	–	0	0	0	0	1
v_5	–	–	–	–	0	1	0	0
v_6	–	–	–	–	–	0	1	0
v_7	–	–	–	–	–	–	0	1
v_8	–	–	–	–	–	–	–	0

6.

Vertex Number	Item Pointer
1	1
2	4
3	9
4	12
5	14
6	16
7	20
8	23

Item Number	Vertex Number	Item Pointer
1	2	2
2	5	3
3	6	0
4	1	5
5	6	6
6	7	7
7	8	8
8	3	0
9	2	10
10	4	11
11	8	0
12	3	13
13	8	0
14	1	15
15	6	0
16	1	17
17	2	18
18	5	19
19	7	0
20	2	21
21	6	22
22	8	0
23	2	24
24	3	25
25	4	26
26	7	0

7. 2

8.

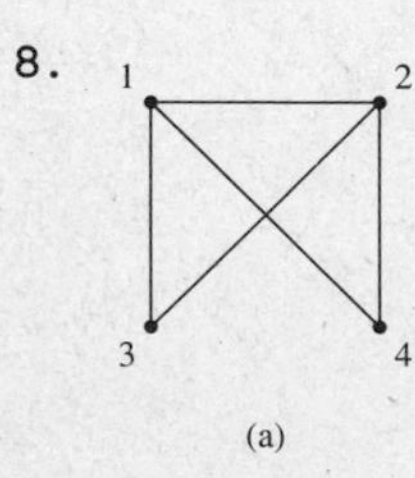

(a)

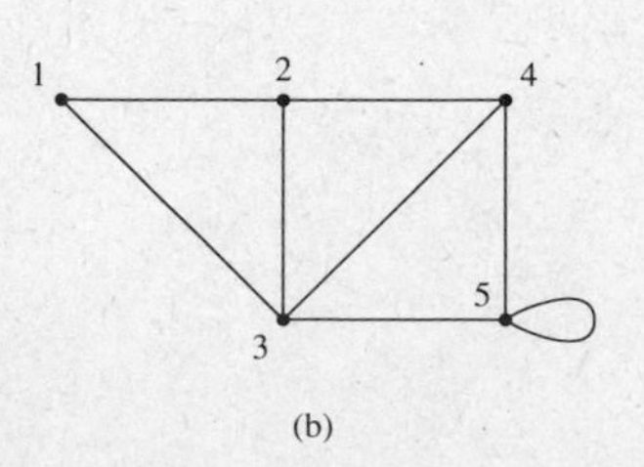

(b)

9.

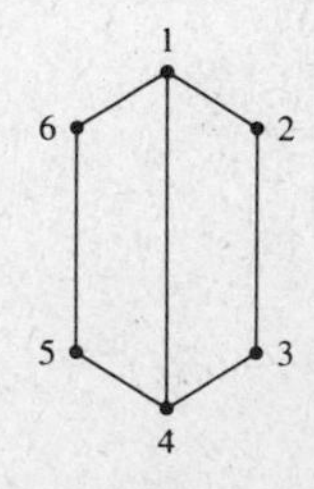

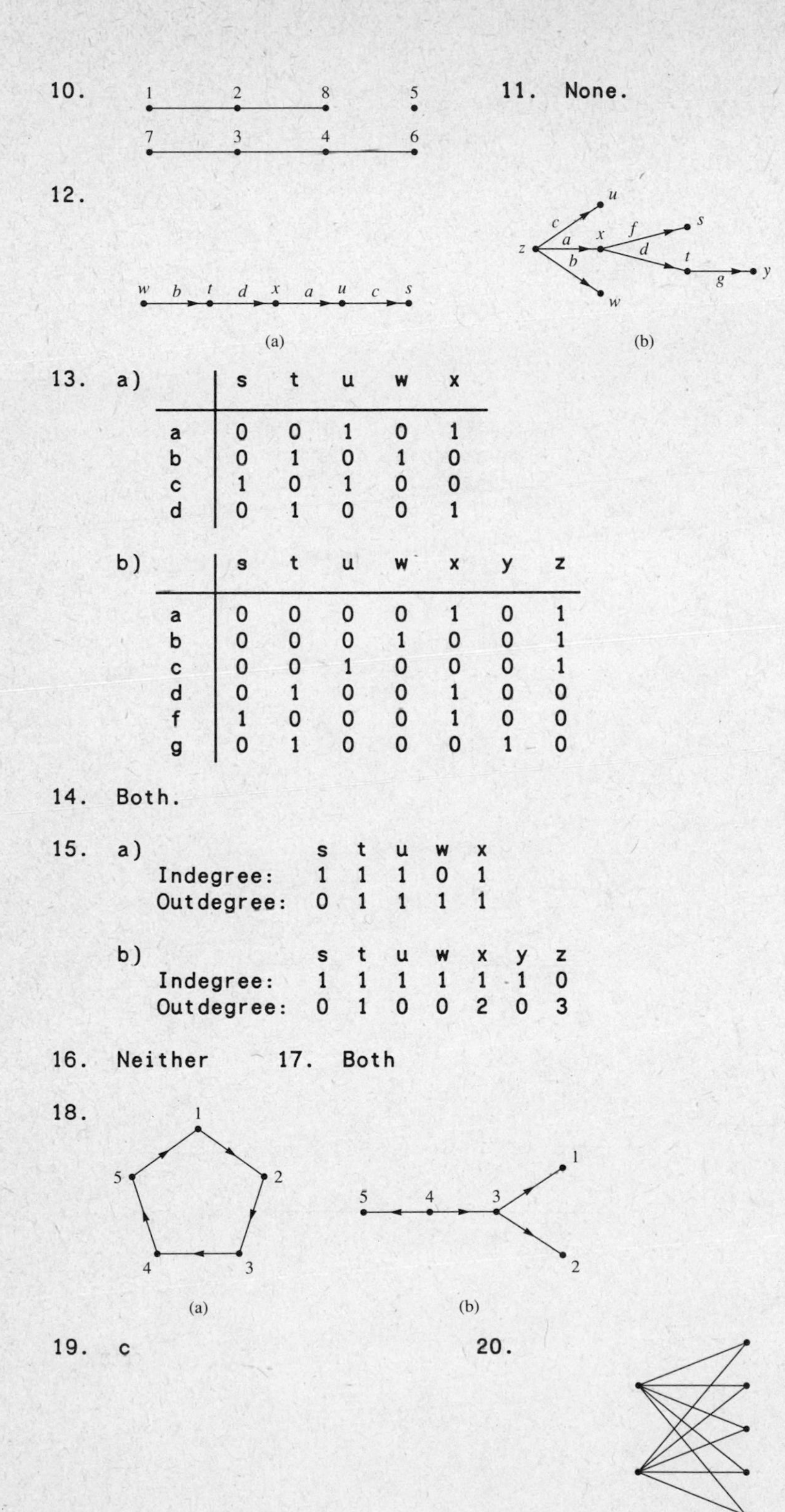

10.

11. None.

12.

(a) (b)

13. a)

	s	t	u	w	x
a	0	0	1	0	1
b	0	1	0	1	0
c	1	0	1	0	0
d	0	1	0	0	1

b)

	s	t	u	w	x	y	z
a	0	0	0	0	1	0	1
b	0	0	0	1	0	0	1
c	0	0	1	0	0	0	1
d	0	1	0	0	1	0	0
f	1	0	0	0	1	0	0
g	0	1	0	0	0	1	0

14. Both.

15. a)

	s	t	u	w	x
Indegree:	1	1	1	0	1
Outdegree:	0	1	1	1	1

b)

	s	t	u	w	x	y	z
Indegree:	1	1	1	1	1	1	0
Outdegree:	0	1	0	0	2	0	3

16. Neither 17. Both

18.

(a) (b)

19. c

20.

21. None; all have two components.

22.

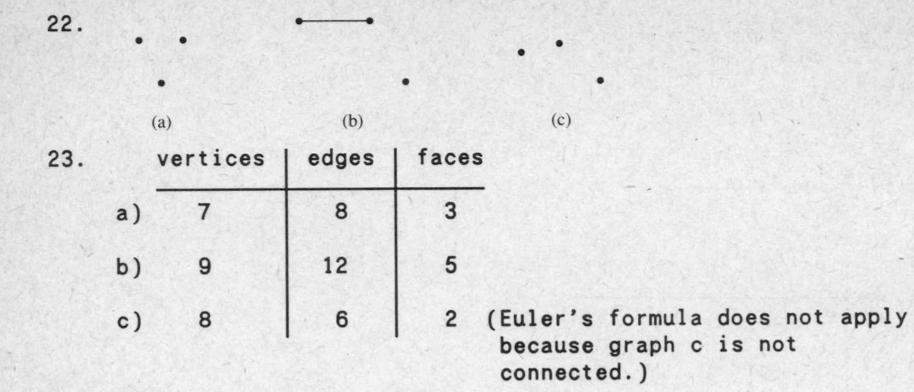

(a) (b) (c)

23.

	vertices	edges	faces
a)	7	8	3
b)	9	12	5
c)	8	6	2 (Euler's formula does not apply because graph c is not connected.)

24.

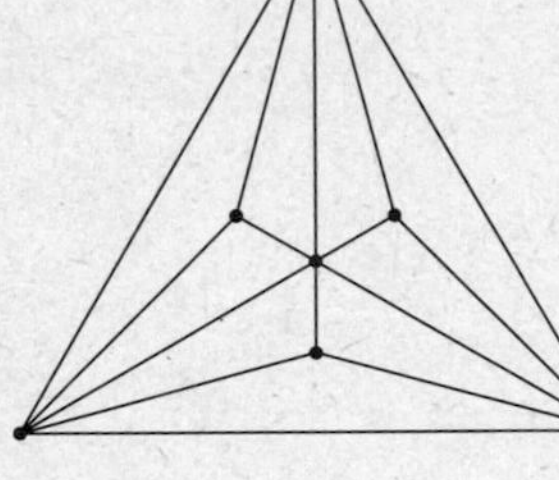

(a)

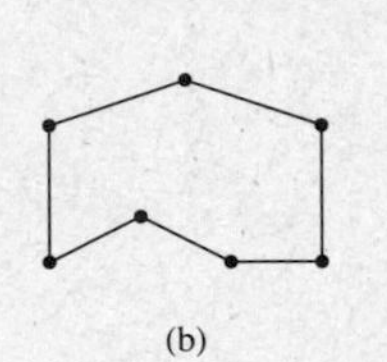

(b)

25.

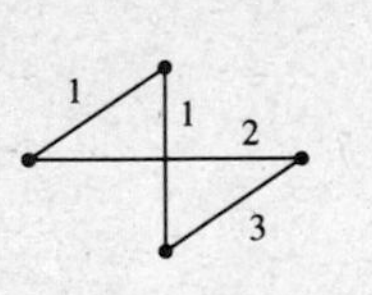

(a)

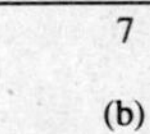

(b)

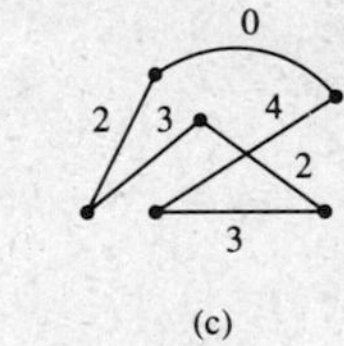

(c)

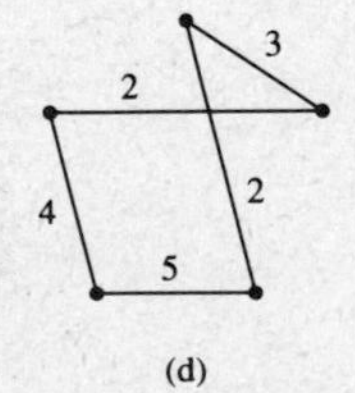

(d)

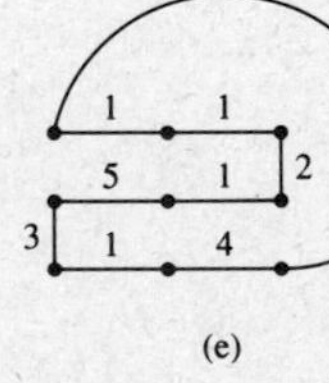

(e)

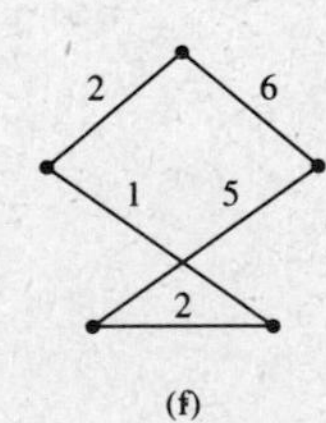

(f)

26.

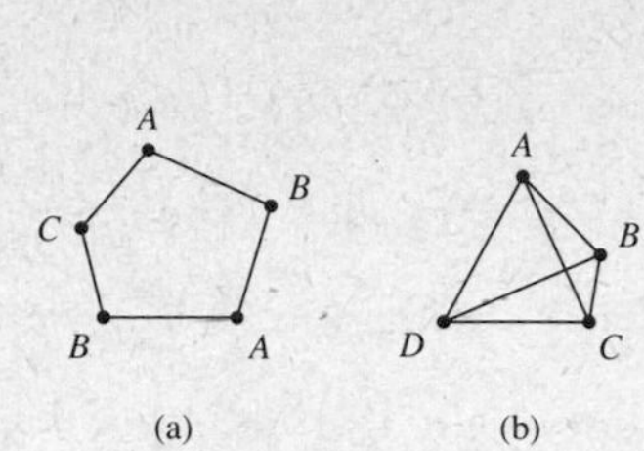

(a) (b)

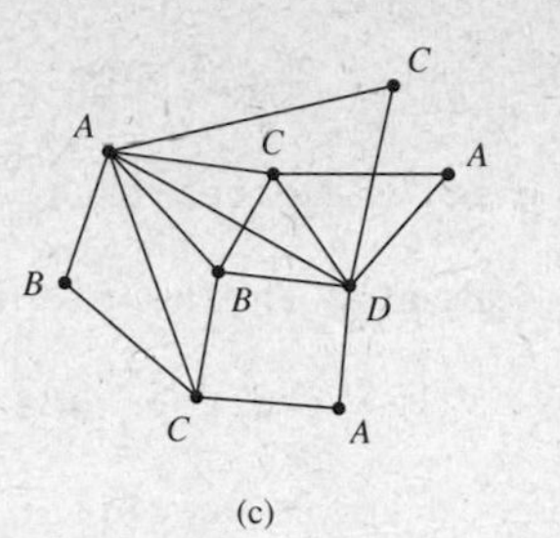

(c)

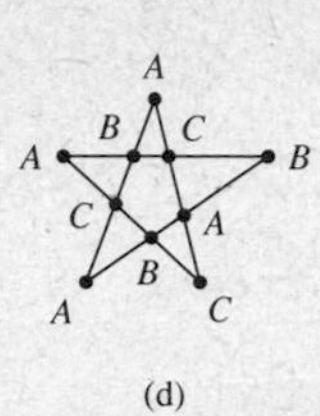

(d)

27.

Step	Sel.	a	b	c	d	e	f	g	h	i
1	a	0	1	∞	2	∞	∞	∞	∞	3
2	b	0	1	2	2	3	∞	∞	∞	3
3	c	0	1	2	2	3	4	∞	∞	3
4	d	0	1	2	2	3	4	5	∞	3
5	e	0	1	2	2	3	4	5	5	3
6	i	0	1	2	2	3	4	5	5	3
7	f	0	1	2	2	3	4	5	5	3
8	g	0	1	2	2	3	4	5	5	3
9	h	0	1	2	2	3	4	5	5	3
	Pred.	–	a	b	a	b	c	d	e	a

28.

Step	Sel.	a	b	c	d	e	f	g	h	i
1	c	∞	1	0	∞	∞	2	∞	∞	∞
2	b	2	1	0	∞	3	2	∞	∞	∞
3	a	2	1	0	4	3	2	∞	∞	5
4	f	2	1	0	4	3	2	∞	∞	5
5	e	2	1	0	4	3	2	∞	5	5
6	d	2	1	0	4	3	2	7	5	5
7	h	2	1	0	4	3	2	6	5	5
8	i	2	1	0	4	3	2	6	5	5
9	g	2	1	0	4	3	2	6	5	5
	Pred.	b	c	–	a	b	c	h	e	a

Chapter 8

Section 8.1

1. a, b

2.

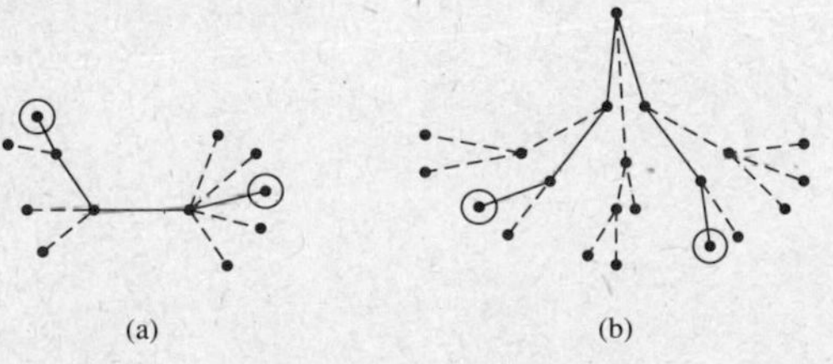

(a) (b)

3. 1 and 2 4. $m = 1$ or $n = 1$

5. We will prove by induction on the number p of vertices, that every tree can be embedded in the plane using straight lines for edges. Step 1: If $p = 1$, the graph is a point. Step 2: If G is a tree with n vertices, let v be a leaf. Let e be the edge to v and let w be the other end of e. Remove v and e. The remainder H is planar by the induction hypothesis. Choose a point in the plane closer to w than any other vertex but not on any edge, call it v, and join it to w with a straight line. The number of faces is 1.

6. Linear graphs. 7. C(n,2)

8. 2, because two colors can be made to alternate along each path.

9.

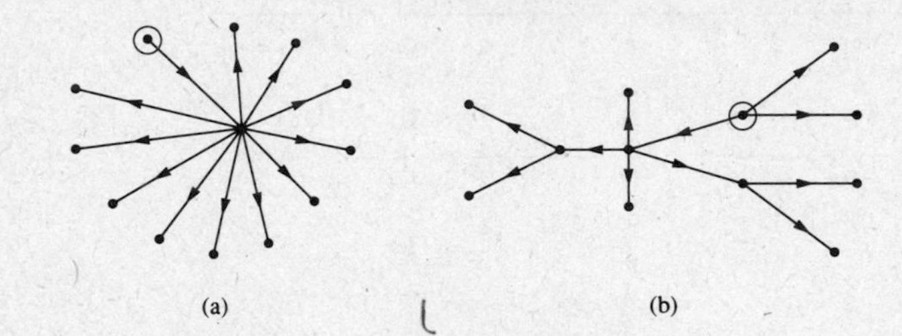

10. b; the root is at the lower left.

11.

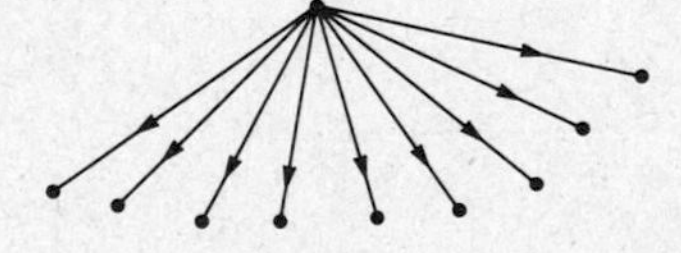

12.

13.

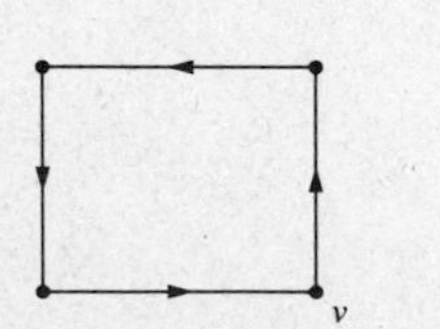

14.

	Vertex	Children	Parent	Siblings
a)	a	b,c,d	none	none
	b	e,f,g,h	a	c,d
	c	i	a	b,d
	d	j,k,l	a	b,c
	e	none	b	f,g,h
	f	none	b	e,g,h
	g	none	b	e,f,h
	h	none	b	e,f,g
	i	m,n	c	none
	j	none	d	k,l
	k	none	d	j,l
	l	none	d	j,k
	m	none	i	n
	n	none	i	m
b)	a	b,c,d,e, f,g,h,i	none	none
	b	none	a	c,d,e,f,g,h,i
	c	none	a	b,d,e,f,g,h,i
	d	none	a	b,c,e,f,g,h,i
	e	none	a	b,c,d,f,g,h,i
	f	j,k,l	a	b,c,d,e,g,h,i
	g	none	a	b,c,d,e,f,h,i
	h	none	a	b,c,d,e,f,g,i
	i	none	a	b,c,d,e,f,g,h
	j	none	f	k,l
	k	none	f	j,l
	l	none	f	j,k
c)	a	b,c	none	none
	b	none	a	c
	c	d,e	a	b
	d	none	c	e
	e	f,g	c	d
	f	none	e	g
	g	h,i	e	f
	h	none	g	i
	i	none	g	h
d)	a	b	none	none
	b	c	a	none
	c	d	b	none
	d	e,f,g	c	none
	e	none	d	f,g
	f	h	d	e,g
	g	none	d	e,f
	h	i	f	none
	i	none	h	none

15. a)

Vertex	Parent	First Child	Next Sibling
a	0	b	0
b	a	e	c
c	a	i	d
d	a	j	0
e	b	0	f
f	b	0	g
g	b	0	h
h	b	0	0
i	c	m	0
j	d	0	k
k	d	0	l
l	d	0	0
m	i	0	n
n	i	0	0

b)

Vertex	Parent	First Child	Next Sibling
a	0	b	0
b	a	0	c
c	a	0	d
d	a	0	e
e	a	0	f
f	a	j	g
g	a	0	h
h	a	0	i
i	a	0	0
j	f	0	k
k	f	0	l
l	f	0	0

c)

Vertex	Parent	First Child	Next Sibling
a	0	b	0
b	a	0	c
c	a	d	0
d	c	0	e
e	c	f	0
f	e	0	g
g	e	h	0
h	g	0	i
i	g	0	0

d)

Vertex	Parent	First Child	Next Sibling
a	0	b	0
b	a	c	0
c	b	d	0
d	c	e	0
e	d	0	f
f	d	h	g
g	d	0	0
h	f	i	0
i	h	0	0

16. a) 3! x 4! x 2! x 3! = 1728 b) 8! x 3! = 241920

c) 2 x 2 x 2 x 2 = 16 d) 3! = 6

17.

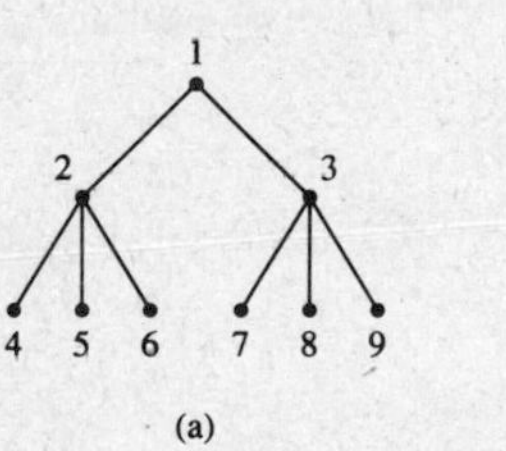

(a)

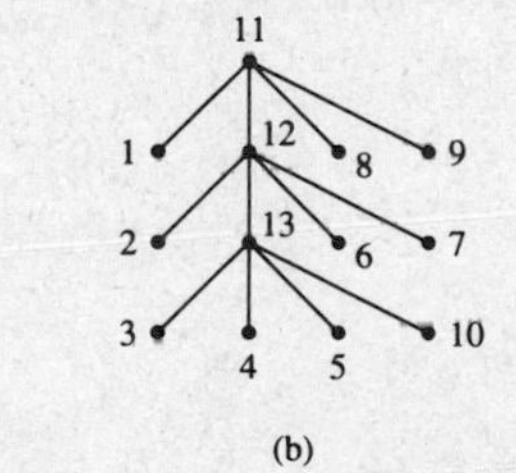

(b)

18.

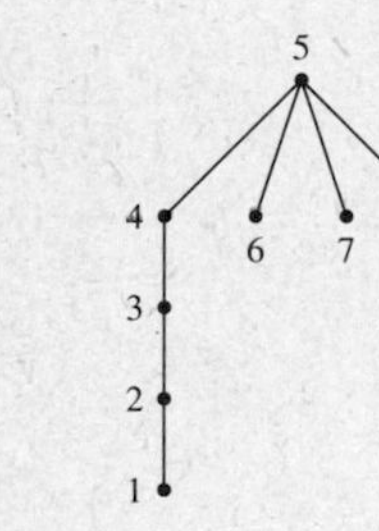

(a)

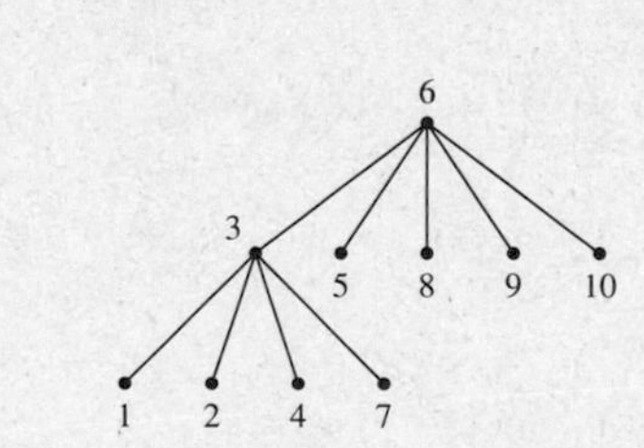

(b)

a)

Vertex	Parent	First Child	Next Sibling
1	2	0	0
2	3	1	0
3	4	2	0
4	5	3	6
5	0	4	0
6	5	0	7
7	5	0	8
8	5	0	0

b)

Vertex	Parent	First Child	Next Sibling
1	3	0	2
2	3	0	4
3	6	1	5
4	3	0	7
5	6	0	8
6	0	3	0
7	3	0	0
8	6	0	9
9	6	0	10
10	6	0	0

Section 8.2

1.

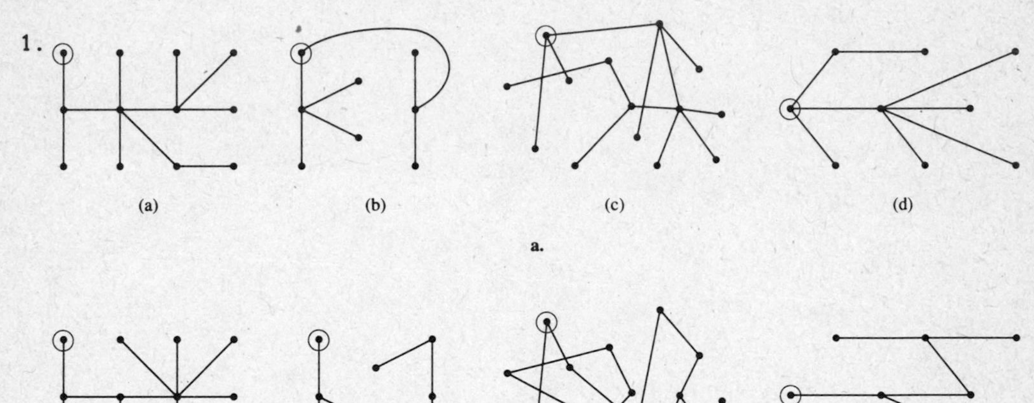

2. An (n-1)-point star
3. A linear graph
4. If the root is on the m-vertex side, it is connected to all n vertices on the other side; one of these is connected to the remaining m-1 vertices on the first side.
5. A linear graph with a star attached to one end.
6. Let a and b be the ends of the edge e. There is a unique path in T from a to b; adding e makes this path into a cycle. Now let C by a cycle in T'. Then C must contain e; for if it did not, it would be a cycle in T, which is impossible. The remainder of C is

a path from a to b in T, and is therefore unique. Now let T" be obtained from T' by deleting any edge of C. Then T" is connected, and has the same number of edges and vertices as T; by Theorem 8.2, T" is a tree.

7\.

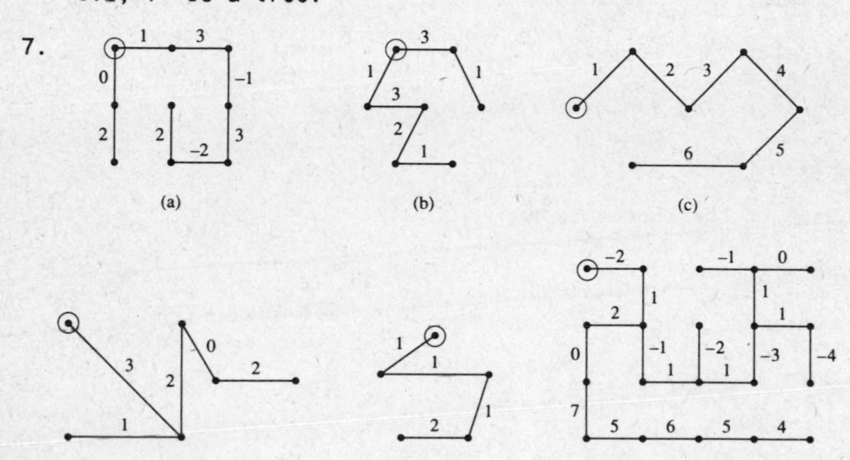

(a) (b) (c) (d) (e) (f)

8\. The results are the same as in Exercise 7.

Section 8.3

1. Greater than 19; greater than 37; less than 43; equal to 41.
2. 10
3. $2^{N+1}-1$ vertices; $2^{N+1}-2$ edges.
4. Greater than 066

   Greater than 101

   Less than 133

   Less than 121 - not found.
5. a) Less then Tell

   Greater than Boccanegra

   Less than Miller

   Greater than Budd

   Less than Lecouvreur

   Greater than Chenier

Greater than Giovanni

Greater than Herring - not found.

b) Less than Tell

Greater than Boccanegra

Greater than Miller

Greater than Schicchi - not found.

c) Less than Tell

Greater than Boccanegra

Less than Miller

Less than Budd - not found.

d) Greater than Tell

Greater than Troyens - not found.

6.

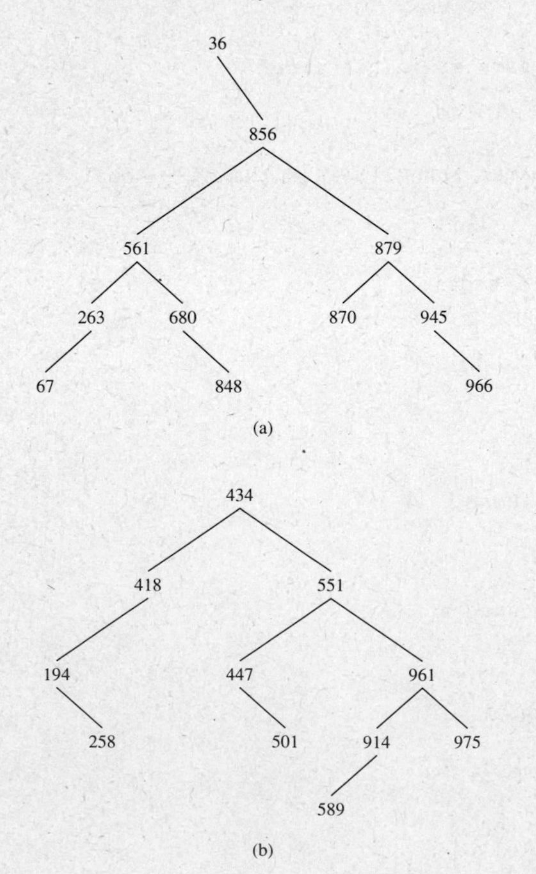

7. Insert Ivnor as right child of Herring

   Insert Stuarta as right child of Schicchi

   Insert Bolena as left child of Budd

   Insert Wozzeck as right child of Troyens

8. Insert 218 as right child of 177

   Insert 018 as left child of 019

   Insert 057 as right child of 037

   Insert 077 as right child of 076

9. A linear graph

10. a)

Vertex	Parent	Left Child	Right Child
1 (Tell)	0	2	5
2 (Boccanegra)	1	0	3
3 (Miller)	2	4	9
4 (Budd)	3	0	6
5 (Troyens)	1	0	0
6 (Lecouvreur)	4	7	11
7 (Chenier)	6	0	8
8 (Giovanni)	7	0	10
9 (Schicchi)	3	12	0
10 (Herring)	8	13	0
11 (Lescaut)	6	0	0
12 (Onegin)	9	0	0
13 (Grimes)	10	0	0

b)

Vertex	Parent	Left Child	Right Child
1 (036)	0	0	2
2 (856)	1	3	4
3 (561)	2	8	6
4 (879)	2	9	5
5 (945)	4	0	7
6 (680)	3	0	10
7 (966)	5	0	0
8 (263)	3	11	0
9 (870)	4	0	0
10 (848)	6	0	0
11 (067)	8	0	0

c)

Vertex	Parent	Left Child	Right Child
1 (434)	0	4	2
2 (551)	1	3	5
3 (447)	2	0	6
4 (418)	1	7	0
5 (961)	2	8	11
6 (501)	3	0	0
7 (194)	4	0	10
8 (914)	5	9	0
9 (589)	8	0	0
10 (258)	7	0	0
11 (975)	5	0	0

Section 8.4

1. a) preorder: abdefhigc

   inorder: dbhfiegac

   postorder: dhifgebca

   b) preorder: abdhlmiecfgjknp

   inorder: lhmdibeafcjgnkp

   postorder: lmhidebfjnpkgca

2. a) preorder: abfgcdhijke

   inorder: fbgacihkjde

   postorder: fgbcikjhdea

   b) preorder: abfhicjkdlmegnp

   inorder: hfibajckldmngpe

   postorder: hifbjkclmdnpgea

3.

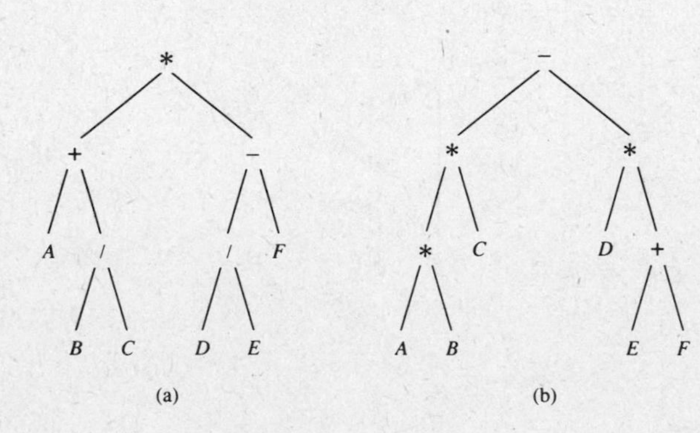

4.

```
(a)            +
              / \
             A   /
                / \
               +   D
              / \
             *   *
            / \ / \
           A  F A  C

(b)            /
              / \
             -   D
            / \
           *   C
          / \
         +   B
        / \
       F   A
```

5. a) (1) *+A/BC-/DEF (2) ABC/+DE/F-*

   b) (1) -*A*BC*D+EF (2) AB*C*DEF+*-

6. a) (1) +A/+*AF*ACD (2) AAF*AC*+D/+

   b) (1) /-*+FABCD (2) FA+B*C-D/

7. a) (1)

A	B	C	/	+	D	E	/	F	-	*
2	3	-1	-3	-1	5	-5	-1	11	-12	12
	2	3	2		-1	5	-1	-1	-1	
		2				-1		-1		

a) (2)

A	B	C	/	+	D	E	/	F	-	*
7	-12	5	-2.4	4.6	5	2	2.5	-21	23.5	108.1
	7	-12	7		4.6	5	4.6	2.5	4.6	
		7				4.6		4.6		

b) (1)

A	B	*	C	*	D	E	F	+	*	-
2	3	6	-1	-6	5	-5	11	6	30	-36
	2		6		-6	5	-5	5	-6	
						-6	5	-6		
							-6			

b) (2)

A	B	*	C	*	D	E	F	+	*	-
7	-12	-84	5	-420	5	2	-21	-19	-95	-325
	7		-84		-420	5	2	5	-420	
						-420	5	-420		
							-420			

8. a) (1)

A	A	F	*	A	C	*	+	D	/	+
2	2	11	22	2	-1	-2	20	5	4	6
	2	2	2	22	2	22	2	20	2	
		2		2	22	2		2		
					2					

a) (2)

A	A	F	*	A	C	*	+	D	/	+
7	7	-21	-147	7	5	35	-112	5	-22.4	-15.4
	7	7	7	-147	7	-147	7	-112	7	
		7		7	-147	7		7		
					7					

b) (1)

F	A	+	B	*	C	-	D	/
11	2	13	3	39	-1	40	5	8
	11		13		39		40	

b) (2)

F	A	+	B	*	C	-	D	/
-21	7	-14	-12	168	5	163	5	32.6
	-21		-14		168		163	

9. AB-* and AB-C*. In the first, "-" must be processed as a unary operation by negating B; in the second, "-" must be processed as a binary operation. To resolve the ambiguity, it is necessary to use different symbols for unary - and binary -. Most calculators have a key labled +/- for unary -; the "-" key is binary -.

10. Yes; the same method works but processing must proceed from right to left.

11. Left children: Boccanegra, Budd, Chenier, Giovanni; right children: Schicchi, Herring. (null), Boccanegra, (null), Budd, (null), Chenier, (null), Giovanni, Grimes, Herring, (null), Lecouvreur, Lescaut, Miller, Onegin, Schicchi, (null), Tell, Troyens.

12.

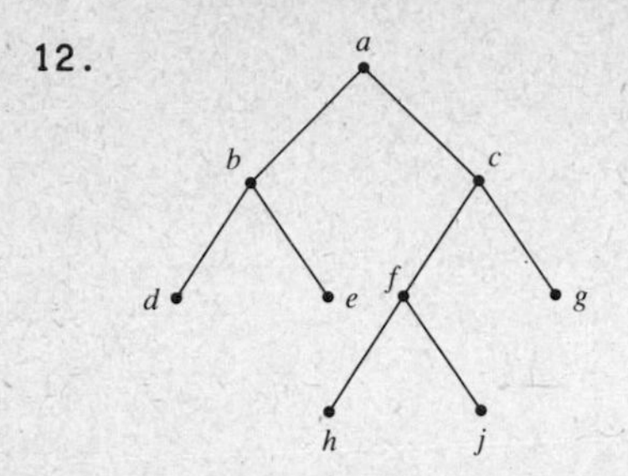

Chapter Review

1.

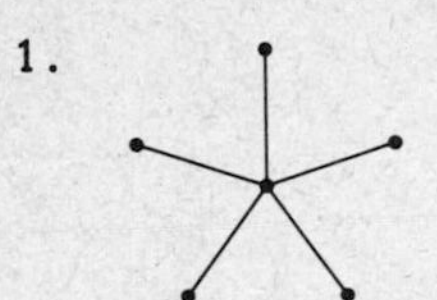

2.

3.

Vertex	Parent	Children	Siblings
a	none	b,c	none
b	a	d,e,f	c
c	a	g,h	b
d	b	none	e,f
e	b	none	d,f
f	b	i	d,e
g	c	none	h
h	c	none	g
i	f	none	none

4. c, d, f

5. c) the entire graph

   d) z to y

   f) 5 to 1 or 5 to 2

6.

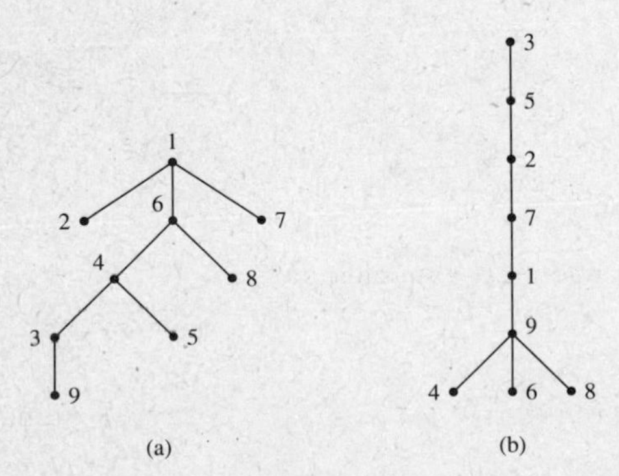

(a) (b)

7.

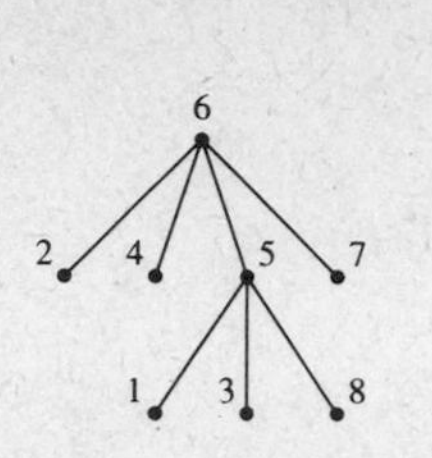

(a)

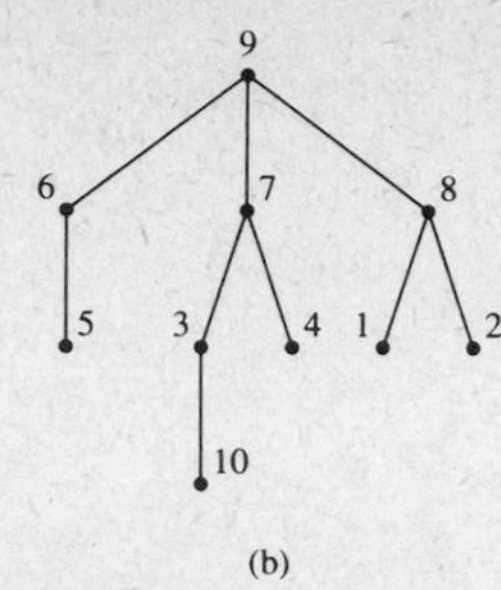

(b)

a)

Vertex	Parent	First Child	Next Sibling
1	5	0	3
2	6	0	4
3	5	0	8
4	6	0	5
5	6	1	7
6	0	2	0
7	6	0	0
8	5	0	0

b)

Vertex	Parent	First Child	Next Sibling
1	8	0	2
2	8	0	0
3	7	10	4
4	7	0	0
5	6	0	0
6	9	5	6
7	9	3	8
8	9	1	0
9	0	6	0
10	3	0	0

8.

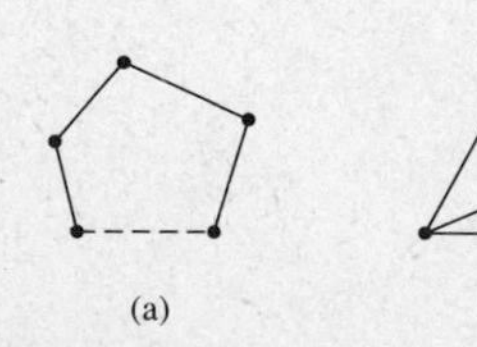

(a)

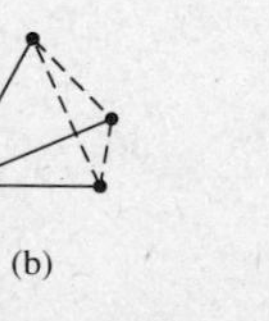

(b)

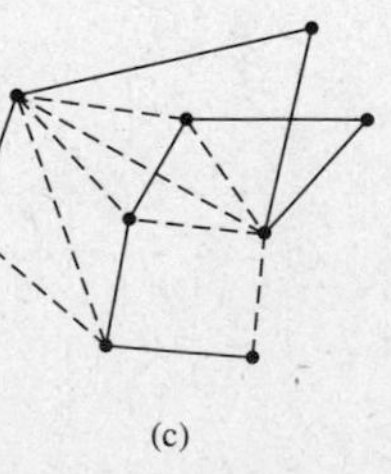

(c)

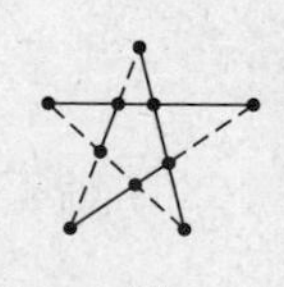

(d)

9. (The result depends on the weights you choose)

10.

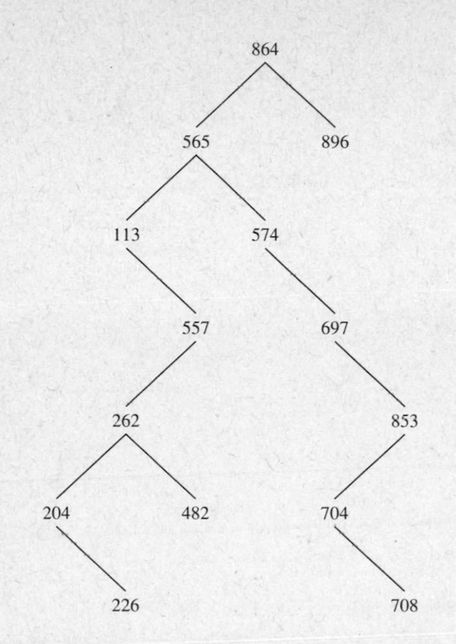

11. (a) Chenier, Miller, Tell, Boccanegra, Troyens, Budd, Lecouvreur, Herring, Schicchi, Giovanni, Onegin, Lescaut, Grimes. (b) Boccanegra, Tell, Budd, Lecouvreur, Troyens, Miller, Giovanni, Schicchi, Lescaut, Grimes, Onegin, Herring, Chenier.

12. (a) Tell, Boccanegra, Miller, Budd, Lecouvreur, Chenier, Giovanni, Herring, Grimes, Lescaut, Schicchi, Onegin, Troyens. (b) Grimes, Herring, Giovanni, Chenier, Lescaut, Lecouvreur, Budd, Onegin, Schicchi, Miller, Boccanegra, Troyens, Tell.

13. (a) None; 6.

(b) Right child for 6; 3, 6, (null).

(c) Left child for 3, right child for 6; (null), 3, 5, 6, (null).

14.

A	5							
B	−1	5						
C	2	−1	5					
D	−2	2	−1	5				
E	10	−2	2	−1	5			
B	−1	10	−2	2	−1	5		
E	10	−1	10	−2	2	−1	5	
A	5	10	−1	10	−2	2	−1	5
/	2	−1	10	−2	2	−1	5	
C	2	2	−1	10	−2	2	−1	5
−	0	−1	10	−2	2	−1	5	
*	0	10	−2	2	−1	5		
+	10	−2	2	−1	5			
*	−20	2	−1	5				
+	−18	−1	5					
*	18	5						
+	23							

15. No; consider a triangle with edges of weights 2, 3, and 4, and start at the vertex opposite the edge of weight 2.

16.

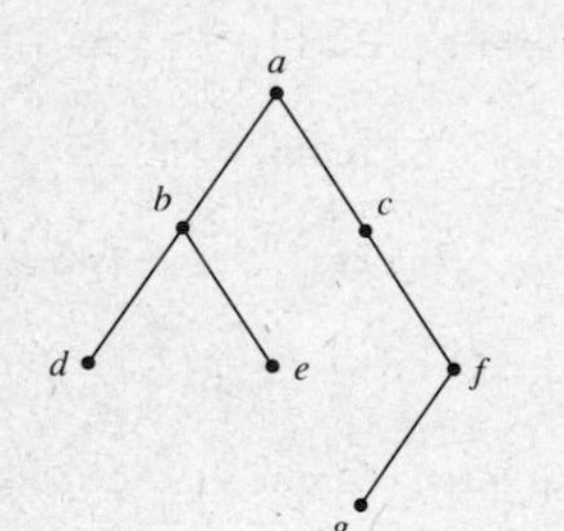

Chapter 9

Section 9.1

1. a) 7, 19, 43, 91,187,379 b) 7, 19, 55, 163, 487, 1459

   c) 2, 2, 2, 2, 2, 2 d) 6, 15, 34, 73, 152, 311

2. a) 5, 13, 41, 121, 365, 1093

   b) −5, −14, −37, −97, −254, −665

   c) 0.5, 3.25, 3.625, 18.0625, 30.78125, 141.8281

3. 1, 2, 3, 5; $s_n = s_{n-1} + s_{n-2}$;

4. $s_n = s_{n-1} + s_{n-2}$; $s_2 = 3$, $s_3 = 5$

5. $s_n = s_{n-1} + s_{n-2} + s_{n-3}$

6. $s_0 = 100$; $s_n = 1.015s_{n-1} + 100 + 10n$; \$2,248.24

7. $s_n = 1.01s_{n-1} - 220$; \$19,876.96

8. $s_n = s_{n-1} + n$

9. $s_n = 1.005s_{n-1} - 1000$

10. 1000, 1100, 1115, 1165, 1203, 1248, 1292, 1339, 1387, 1438, 1489.

The population is growing steadily.

11. $D_n = (n-1)(D_{n-1} + D_{n-2})$

12. Step 1: $D_1 = 0 = 0!(1 - 1/1!)$

Step 2: Assume true for all subscripts $< k$ (strong induction).

Then

$$D_k = (k-1)[D_{k-1} + D_{k-2}]$$

$$= (k-1)[(k-1)!(1 - 1/1! + 1/2! + \ldots +(-1)^{k-1}/(k-1)!)$$
$$+ (k-2)!(1 - 1/1! + 1/2! + \ldots +(-1)^{k-2}/(k-2)!)]$$

$$= (k-1)(k-2)!$$
$$[(k-1)(1 - 1/1! + 1/2! + \ldots +(-1)^{k-1}/(k-1)!)$$
$$+ (1 - 1/1! + 1/2! + \ldots +(-1)^{k-2}/(k-2)!)]$$

$$= (k-1)(k-2)!$$
$$[k - k/1! + k/2! + \ldots +k(-1)^{k-1}/(k-1)!$$
$$- 1 + 1/1! - 1/2! + \ldots +(-1)^{k}/(k-1)!$$
$$+ 1 - 1/1! + 1/2! + \ldots +(-1)^{k-2}/(k-2)!\ ]$$

$$= (k-1)(k-2)!$$
$$[k - k/1! + k/2! + \ldots +k(-1)^{k-1}/(k-1)! + (-1)^{k}/(k-1)!]$$

$$= k(k-1)(k-2)!$$
$$[1 - 1/1! + 1/2! + \ldots +(-1)^{k-1}/(k-1)! +(-1)^{k}/k(k-1)!]$$

$$= k![1 - 1/1! + 1/2! + \ldots +(-1)^{k}/(k)!]$$

13. Step 1: $b_0 = 1 = 2^0$. Step 2: assume $b_{n-1} = 2^{n-1}$. Then $b_n = 2(b_{n-1})$ $= 2(2^{n-1}) = 2^n$.

14. Step 1: $c_1 = 1 = 2^1 - 1$. Step 2: assume $c_{n-1} = 2^{n-1} - 1$. Then $c_n =$

$2(2^{n-1} - 1) + 1 = 2^n - 2 + 1 = 2^n - 1.$

15. a) $a_n = (1 - \alpha - \beta)a_{n-1} + 2\beta a_{n-2}$

    b) $b_n = (1 - \alpha - \beta)b_{n-1} + 2\beta b_{n-2}$

    c) $s_n = (1 - \alpha - \beta)s_{n-1} + 2\beta s_{n-2}$

16. $c_n = c_{n-1} + n$

17. The probability is $D_n/n!$; see Exercise 11.

Section 9.2

1.

	Order	Linear	Homogeneous	Const. Coeff.
a)	2	No		
b)	3	Yes	Yes	Yes
c)	2	No		

2.

	Order	Linear	Homogeneous	Const. Coeff.
a)	3	Yes	No	Yes
b)	2	Yes	No	No
c)	4	Yes	Yes	Yes

3. a) $s_n = 3^n(-3) + 1 = 1 - 3^{n+1}$

   b) $s_n = 5 + 2n$

   c) $s_n = -3(0.5)^n + 4$

   d) $s_n = 10(-0.1)^n$

4. a) $s_n = -0.75(0.2)^n + 0.5$

   b) $s_n = -(-1)^n/2 + 1/2$

   c) $s_n = -(-1)^n/2 + 3/2$

5. $s_n = -2000(1.01)^n + 22000$

6. $s_n = -100000(1.005)^n + 200000$

7. Only when $b = 0$; then all points are fixed points.

8. Yes; 1/3

9. Yes; $(3 \pm \sqrt{5})/2$

10. Step 1: If $n = 0$, $s_0 = a^0 s_0$.

    Step 2: $s_n = as_{n-1} + b$

$$= a(a^{n-1}s_0 + b \sum_{i=0}^{n-2} a^i) + b$$

$$= a^n s_0 + b(a \sum_{i=0}^{n-2} a^i + 1) = a^n s_0 + b \sum_{i=0}^{n-1} a^i$$

11. The even and odd terms, considered separately, are defined by linear inhomogeneous recurrence relations with constant coefficients. Therefore, the techniques of this section may be applied to the even and odd terms. The result is:

    even terms: $s_{2n} = 2^n(5/4) + 3/4$

    odd terms: $s_{2n+1} = 2^n(-1/4) + 3/4$

Section 9.3

1. a) $x + 15$ b) $x^2 + 6x - 5$ c) $x^3 - x^2 - 7x + 13$

2. $F_4 = 1/\sqrt{5}[((1+\sqrt{5})/2)^4 - ((1-\sqrt{5})/2)^4]$

   $= 1/\sqrt{5}[(1+2\sqrt{5}+5)^2/16 - (1-2\sqrt{5}+5)^2/16]$

   $= 1/\sqrt{5}[(6+2\sqrt{5})^2/16 - (6-2\sqrt{5})^2/16]$

   $= 1/\sqrt{5}[(36+24\sqrt{5}+20)/16 - (36-24\sqrt{5}+20)/16]$

   $= 1/\sqrt{5}[1/16((56+24\sqrt{5}) - (56-24\sqrt{5}))]$

   $= 1/16\sqrt{5}(48\sqrt{5}) = 48/16 = 3$

3. $5s_{n-1} - 6s_{n-2} = 5A(2)^{n-1} + 5B(3)^{n-1} - 6A(2)^{n-2} - 6B(3)^{n-2}$

   $= A(2)^{n-2}[5(2)-6] + B(3)^{n-2}[5(3)-6]$

   $= A(2)^{n-2}(4) + B(3)^{n-2}(9)$

   $= A(2)^{n-2}(2^2) + B(3)^{n-2}(3^2)$

   $= A(2)^n + B(3)^n$

   $= s_n$

4. $s_n = (8/3)(1/2)^n - (2/3)(-1/4)^n$

5. $s_n = 4(1/2)^n - 2(-1/2)^n$

6. $a_n = 7500/7 - (500/7)(-2/5)^n$

7. $a_n = 1108.32(0.962)^n - 108.32(-0.312)^n$

8. $s_n = (-1/2)^n(4 - 12n)$

9. $s_n = (1 + i/2)(1+i)^n + (1 - i/2)(1-i)^n$

10. $s_n = 1/2 + 2^n - 3^n/2$

11. $s_n = (2/9)2^n + (1/6)n2^n - (2/9)(-1)^n$

12. Since $s_0 = a$; $s_1 = b$,

$$A + B = a \text{ and}$$

$$Ai - Bi = b$$

Multiplying the first equation by i and adding yields

$$2Ai = ai + b$$

so $A = (ai + b)/2i = (ai + b)(-2i)/[2i(-2i)]$

$= (ai + b)(-2i)/(-4i^2) = (ai + b)(-2i)/4$

$= (-2ai^2 - 2bi)/4 = (a - bi)/2$

and $B = a - A$ so that

$$B = a - (a - bi)/2 = (2a - a + bi)/2 = (a + bi)/2$$

The first six terms are: a, b, -a, -b, a, b

13. With any set of initial conditions, the solution is a periodic sequence with period 3. This is because the roots of the characteristic equation are the cube roots of 1.

Section 9.4

1. $s_n = 2(1/2)^n + n - 1$

2. $s_n = -405(1.01)^n + 5n + 505$

3. a) $s_n = 5 + (n^2 + n)/2$

   b) $s_n = -3 + (n^2 + n)/2$

4. $s_n = (32/9)(-1/2)^n - (32/3)n(-1/2)^n + 4/9$

5. $s_n = (-1 - i/2)(1 + i)^n + (-1 + i/2)(1 - i)^n - 2n + 4$

6. $s_n = -(1/3)(-1)^n - (2/3)2^n + (1/2)n2^n + 1$

7. $a = 1$

8. $a + b = 1$ and $c \neq 0$

9. $a = 2$, $b = -1$, and $c \neq 0$

10. $(1/3)n^3 + (1/2)n^2 + (1/6)n$

Section 9.6

1. a) 2 b) 6/5

2. a) 25/16 b) 1/768

3. a) $s_n = -1 + 2^n$

   b) $s_n = (3/2)(1/2)^n - (1/2)(-1/2)^n$

   c) $s_n = (3/5)2^n + (2/5)(-1/2)^n$

4. a) $s_n = n + 2$

   b) $s_n = -7(2)^n + (7/2)(3)^n + n + 7/2$

5. Choose $M = 14$. Then $13n + 7 \leq 14(n - 15) = 14n - 210$ whenever $n \geq 217$. Thus, you can choose $n_0 = 217$.

6. Choose $M = 1$. Then $n + 20 \leq 1(n^2 - 4)$ is equivalent to $n^2 - n - 24 \geq 0$, that is, $n \geq (1 \pm \sqrt{97})/2$. So let $n_0 = 6$.

7. Choose $M = 4$. Then $3n^2 + 2 \leq 4(n^2 - 10) = 4n^2 - 40$ is equivalent to $-n^2 \leq -42$, that is, $n^2 \geq 42$

   So choose $n_0 = 7$.

8. $f(1/n) = a_k(1/n)^k + a_{k-1}(1/n)^{k-1} + \ldots + a_1(1/n) + a_0$

   $\leq (|a_k| + |a_{k-1}| + \ldots + |a_0|)$ for $n \geq 1$

   Let $(|a_k| + |a_{k-1}| + \ldots + |a_0|)$ be M.

9. By Exercise 2 of Section 2.7, $n \leq 2^n$ for $n \geq 1$. So, taking $n_0 = 0$ and $M = 1$:

   $$\log_2(n) \leq 2^{\log_2(n)} = n$$

10. If $a \leq c$, then $an + b \leq cn + d$ for $n \geq n_0$. So $an - cn \leq d - b \Rightarrow n \geq (d-b)/(a-c)$. Therefore, choose

$n_0 = (d-b)/(a-c)$.

Showing that $g \epsilon O(f)$ is similar.

11. Given any n_0 and M, choose n such that $n \geq n_0$ and $n > M$.

12. As shown in Exercise 15, Section 9.1, the number of steps s_n satisfies $s_n = s_{n-1} + n$ with $s_1 = 1$. The solution of this recurrence relation is $s_n = (n^2 + n)/2 \epsilon O(n^2)$.

13. We may always add more numbers so that the number of items to be sorted is a power of 2, so we will only consider the case $n = 2^m$. Let t_m be the number of steps required to sort 2^m items. Then $t_m = 2t_{m-1} + 2^m$. We want to show that $t_m \epsilon O(n \log_2(n)) = O(m2^m)$. That is, we want to show that $t_m \leq Mm2^m$ for all m and some M. This will be proved by induction. Step 1: for m = 1, just take $M = t_1$. Step 2: assume that $t_{m-1} \leq M2^{m-1}(m-1)$. Then $t_m = 2t_{m-1} + 2^m \leq 2M2^{m-1}(m-1) + 2^m = 2^m[M(m-1) + 1] \leq 2^m Mm$.

14. a) $0 + 1 + \ldots + n = n(n + 1)/2$ b) n

    c) These are $O(n^2)$ and $O(n)$ respectively.

Chapter Review

1. a) 15.5, 19.25, 24.875, 33.3125

   b) 1.5, 0.75, 1.125, 0.9375

   c) 3/2, 5/3, 8/5, 13/8 d) 0, 3, -2, 9

2. a) -1, 2, -3, 5 b) 2, 9, 38, 161 c) 6, 21, 138, 801

3. 1, 2, 4, 7; $s_n = s_{n-1} + s_{n-2} + s_{n-3}$

4. $s_1 = 1$, $s_2 = 4$, $s_3 = 7$, $s_n = s_{n-1} + s_{n-2} + s_{n-3}$

5. $s_1 = 1$, $s_2 = 4$, $s_3 = 7$, $s_n = s_{n-1} + s_{n-2} + 1$

6. $a_n = 1.06a_{n-1} + 300$; $a_0 = \$100$; $a_{12} = \$5,262.20$

7. $a_n = 1.01a_{n-1} - 1100$, $a_0 = \$80,000$; $a_8 = \$77,514.30$

8. $a_n = 1.005833a_{n-1} - 1200$; $a_0 = \$150,000$.

9. a) order 2, non-linear

   b) order 5, linear, homogeneous, constant coefficients

   c) order 2, non-linear

   d) order 2, linear, non-homogeneous, constant coefficients

10. a) $s_n = 36(1.2)^n - 35$ b) $s_n = (1/4)(-3)^n - 1/4$

    c) $s_n = 10 - 2n$ d) $s_n = (54/11)(-0.1)^n + 1/11$

11. $2 \pm \sqrt{2}$

12. a) $x - 13$ b) $x^2 - 5x + 4$ c) $x^3 + x^2 + 6x + 21$

13. $F_n = (1/\sqrt{5})[(1 + \sqrt{5})/2]^n - (1/\sqrt{5}([(1 - \sqrt{5})/2]^n$; since

    $(1 - \sqrt{5})/2 = -0.62$, the second term is always less than

    1/2.

14. $s_n = (5/4)(3)^n - 1/4$

15. $s_n = [(31+4\sqrt{31})/62][(1+\sqrt{31})/5]^n$

    $- [(31 - 4\sqrt{31})/62][(1-\sqrt{31})/5]^n$

16. $s_n = 2(1/2)^n + n(1/2)^n + 3n^2(1/2)^n$

17. $a_0 = 1500$, and $a_1 = 0.6a_0 + 200 = 1100$.

    $a_n = 1214.29 + 285.71(-0.4)^n$

18. $a_0 = 1500$, and $a_1 = 0.65a_0 + 200 = 1175$.

    $a_n = 1289.724(0.9619)^n + 210.276(-0.3119)^n$

19. $s_n = (-2/3)n(3/2)^n$

20. $s_n = -2i[(1+i)/2]^n + 2i[(1-i)/2]^n$

21. $s_n = 4(1/2)^n - 2$

22. $s_n = (2/3)2^n - (1/2)n2^n + (1/3)(-1)^n$

23. $s_n = 2(1/2)^n + 2n - 2$

24. $s_n = -10.1(2)^n + 0.05n + 0.1$

25. a) $s_n = -(n^2 + n)/2$

    b) $s_n = 10 - (n^2 + n)/2$

26. $s_n = (-8/3)n(1.5)^n + 4$

27. $s_n = (i/2 - 1)(1 + i)^n + (-i/2 - 1)(1 - i)^n + n + 2$

28. $s_n = -(2)^n + (1/2)n(2)^n + 1$

29. a) 8/3 b) 1/30 c) -7/3 d) 16/27

30. a) $s_n = (1/2)(1 + i\sqrt{3})^n + (1/2)(1 - i\sqrt{3})^n$

b) $s_n = (2/3)3^n + (1/3)(-3)^n$

c) $s_n = ((5 + 3\sqrt{5})/10)((1 + \sqrt{5})/2)^n$

$+ ((5 - 3\sqrt{5})/10)((1 - \sqrt{5})/2)^n - 1$

d) $s_n = (-3/8)(-3)^n + (1/2)n + 3/8$

31. Choose M = 2. Then $3n^2 + 2n + 1 \leq 2(2n^2 - 10)$ whenever $0 \leq n^2 - 2n - 20$, and this is true provided $n \geq 6$. So choose $n_0 = 6$.

32. a) Choose M = 1, $n_0 = 3$.

b) If $g \in O(f)$, then there exist M > 0 and $n_0 > 0$ such that if $n \geq n_0$, $n^3 - 4 \leq M(n^2 + 2)$; it follows that for such n, $n^3 \leq M(n^2 + 2) + 4 \leq 3Mn^2$ (for large enough n); and this is wrong.

33. $|f(n)| \leq 1$ for all n

34. The solution of the recurrence relation is $s_n = (n^2 + n)/2$ which is $\in O(n^2)$.

Chapter 10

Section 10.1

1. b, c, e

2. a) 5 b) 1 c) 11

3. a) 1 b) 1 c) 12

4. b) If $a|b$ and $a|c$ then there exist integers x and y such that $b = ax$ and $c = ay$; so $b + c = a(x + y)$ and $b - c = a(x - y)$.

c) If $a|b$ and $b|c$ then there exist integers x and y such that

$b = ax$ and $c = by$; so $c = axy$.

d) If $a|b$, then there exists an integer x such that $b = ax$; then $bc = acx$. Conversely, if $ac|bc$, then there exists an integer x such that $bc = acx$. If $c \neq 0$, then $b = ax$.

5. No; $4|(2 \times 2)$ but 4 does not divide 2.

6. No; $2|(3 + 1)$ and $2|(3 - 1)$, but 2 does not divide 3 or 1.

7. If d divides a, b, and c, then there exist integers u, v, and w such that $a = ud$, $b = vd$, and $c = wd$. Then $ax + by + cz = d(ux + vy + wz)$.

8. If $a|b$, $b|c$, and $c|d$, then there exist integers x, y, and z such that $b = ax$, $c = by$, and $d = cz$. Then $d = axyz$.

9. If $x|(a + b)$ and $x|(a - b)$, then by Theorem 10.1(b), $x|2a$ and $x|2b$. Since $(a,b) = 1$, $(2a,2b) = 2$; so by Theorem 10.3, $x|2$.

10. If $x|a$ and $x|(a + 2)$, then $x|2$, so the gcd is 1 or 2.

11. Clearly any common divisor of a and b divides m and n. Solving the system for x and y yields $a = xm + un$, $b = ym + vn$, so any common divisor of m and n divides a and b.

12. If $a/b + c/d$ is an integer, then $bd|(ad + bc)$. It follows that $b|(ad + bc)$, and hence $b|ad$. Since $(a,b) = 1$, $b|d$. Similarly, $d|b$.

13. The proof is by induction. Step 1: $(1,1) = 1$. Step 2: assume that a and b are consecutive terms and that $(a,b) = 1$. The next term is $c = a + b$. If $x|b$ and $x|c$, then $x|(c - b)$, that is, $x|a$. Therefore, $x = 1$.

14. All quotients are 1 and you run back down the series.

15. $(a,b)[a,b] = |ab|$

16. There is an integer x such that $a - b = kx$. Therefore, any common

divisor of a and k divides b, and conversely.

17. Write out the algorithm for a and b:

$$a = bq_1 + r_1 \qquad a/b = q_1 + r_1/b$$

$$b = r_1q_2 + r_2 \qquad b/r_1 = q_2 + r_2/r_1$$

$$r_1 = r_2q_3 + r_3 \qquad r_1/r_2 = q_3 + r_3/r_2$$

$$\ldots \qquad \ldots$$

$$r_{n-2} = r_{n-1}q_n + r_n \quad \text{where } r_n = 1;$$

$$r_{n-1} = r_nq_{n+1} + 0$$

Then

$$g(a/b) = 2^{q_1}g(r_1/b) = 2^{q_1}(1 + g(b/r_1))$$

$$g(b/r_1) = 2^{q_2}g(r_2/r_1) = 2^{q_2}(1 + g(r_1/r_2)$$

$$\ldots$$

$$g(r_{n-1}/r_n) = g(r_{n-1}) = 2^{r_{n-1}}$$

From this, g(a/b) can be computed by repeated substitution from bottom to top. For instance, to compute g(13/5),

$$13 = 5(2) + 1 \qquad g(13/5) = 2^2(1 + g(5/3))$$

$$5 = 3(1) + 2 \qquad g(5/3) = 2^1(1 + g(3/2))$$

$$3 = 2(1) + 1 \qquad g(3/2) = 2^1(1 + g(2/1))$$

$$g(2) = 2^{2-1} = 2$$

and substitution yields g(13/5) = 60.

18. a) $a = bq + r$, so $a \geq b + r$. Since $r < b$, $r < a/2$.

b) Part (a) applies to each step, that is, $r_{k+1} < r_{k-1}/2$. Therefore $r_kr_{k+1} < r_{k-1}r_k/2$.

c) From part (b), in at most $\log_2(ab)$ steps the dividend-divisor product is reduced to 1 and the Euclidean algorithm must end. So note that $\log_2(ab) = \log_2(a) + \log_2(b) \leq 2 \log_2(a)$

Section 10.2

1. a) $2\cdot3\cdot5\cdot7\cdot11$ b) $2^4\cdot3^3\cdot11$

   c) $2\cdot3^2\cdot5\cdot7^2\cdot11$ d) $3^2\cdot5^3\cdot7\cdot11$

   e) $2^2\cdot3^2\cdot5^3\cdot7^3$ f) $2^5\cdot3^4\cdot5^3\cdot7^2\cdot11$

2. a) g.c.d $= 3\cdot5\cdot7\cdot11 = 1,155$

   l.c.m $= 2\cdot3^2\cdot5^3\cdot7\cdot11 = 173,250$

   b) g.c d $= 2^2\cdot3^2 = 36$

   l.c.m $= 2^4\cdot3^3\cdot5^3\cdot7^3\cdot11 = 203,742,000$

   c) g.c.d.$= 2\cdot3^2\cdot5\cdot7^2\cdot11 = 48,510$

   l.c.m. $= 2^5\cdot3^4\cdot5^3\cdot7^2\cdot11 = 174,636,000$

   d) g.c.d. $= 3^2\cdot11 = 99$

   l.c.m. $= 2^4\cdot3^3\cdot5^3\ 7\cdot11 = 4,158,000$

3. Step 1: $n = 2$ is Theorem 10.9. Step 2: assume that if p divides a product of n−1 factors then it divides one of them. If $x = a_1...a_{n-1}a_n$; then by Theorem 10.9, either $p|a_n$ or $p|a_1...a_{n-1}$; in the latter case, apply the induction hypothesis.

4. a) 32 b) 40 c) 72

   d) 48 e) 144 f) 720

5. a) 6,912 b) 14,880 c) 160,056

   d) 194,688 e) 5,678,400 f) 813,404,592

6. $2(n_1 + 1)...(n_k + 1)$ where the n_i are the exponents of the prime factors.

7. 0

8. If $(a,b) = 1$, then the prime factors of a and of b are different; the result follows from the formula in the text.

9. Let $n = 2^{p-1}(2^p - 1)$ and let $q = 2^p - 1$. Then

   $\sigma(n) = q(q + 1) = q(2^p) = 2(2^{p-1})q = 2n$.

10. 6; 28; 496; 8,128; 33,550,336

11. a)

n =	1	2	3	4	5	6	7	8	9	10	11	12
$\phi(n)$ =	1	1	2	2	4	2	6	4	6	4	10	4

b) $p - 1$

c) The numbers not relatively prime to p^k are the multiples of p, of which there are $p^k/p = p^{k-1}$ in the range 1 to p^k.

12. a) By the inclusion-exclusion principle,

$\phi(n) = n - \Sigma n/p_i + \Sigma n/p_ip_j - \Sigma n/p_ip_jp_k + \ldots$ etc.

which is equal to the given product.

b) This follows from the equation in part a), since a and b contain different sets of primes.

13. n and 1 are divisors of n, so if $\sigma(n) = n + 1$, there can be no other positive divisors.

14. a) 480 b) 1,440 c) 10,080

d) 36,000 e) 352,800 f) 36,288,000

Section 10.3

1. a) No b) N c) No

d) $x = -6$, $y = -37$ e) $x = 0$, $y = -3$

2. a) $x = 0$, $y = 0$ b) $x = 10, y = -5$

c) $x = 78$, $y = -416$ d) $x = 946$, $y = -8586$

3. Since p is prime, every x with $1 \leq x < p$ is relatively prime to p.

4. Every x with $1 \leq x < p$ is relatively prime to n; therefore n is prime.

5. [1], [2], [4], [7], [8], [11], [13], [14]

6. All [x] with $1 \leq x < 25$ and x not a multiple of 5.

7. [4] and [5] respectively.

8. [53]

Section 10.4

1. a) $x = 1 + 17t$, $y = 1 + 20t$

   b) $x = -6 + 13t$, $y = -3 + 7t$

   c) $x = 14 + 17t$, $y = -10 - 12t$

2. a) $(x,y) = (0,10)$, $(2,5)$ and $(4,0)$

   b) $x = 13t - 6$, $y = 7t - 3$ for $t \geq 1$

   c) None

3. If x divides a, b, and c, then $x|(a,b)$ and $x|c$ so $x|((a,b),c)$.

   Converely, if $x|((a,b),c)$, then $x|(a,b)$, so x divides a, b, and c.

4. a) 7   b) 13   c) 1   d) 1

5. 7 pads, 5 pens.

6. 16 9-foot sections and 5 17-foot sections

7. No.

8. 28

9. 350 days after feeding the boa constrictor the first time.

10. 15,621. (The equation is $1024x - 15625y = 11529$)

Section 10.5

1. a) $x = -8$, $y = 25$ b) $x = -4$, $y = 10$ c) $x = -30$, $y = 69$

2. a) $x = 7514$, $y = 1751$ b) None

Section 10.6

1. a) [7, 3, 5, 7]   b) [-3, 13, 2, 12, 4]

2. a) $$1 + \cfrac{1}{2 + \cfrac{1}{3 + \cfrac{1}{4 + \cfrac{1}{5}}}}$$ a) $$-1 + \cfrac{1}{3 + \cfrac{1}{2 + \cfrac{1}{16}}}$$

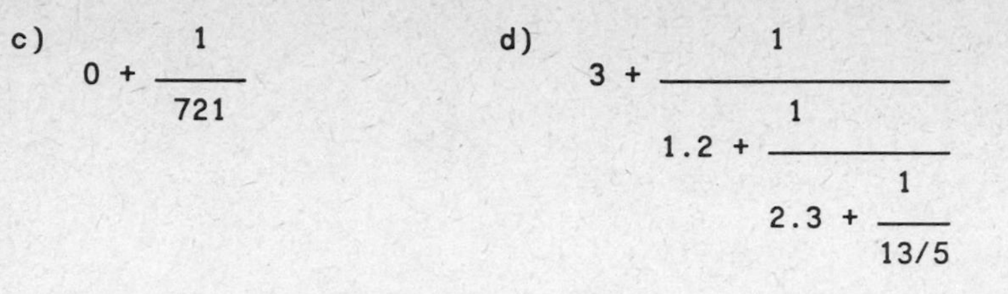

c) $0 + \cfrac{1}{721}$ d) $3 + \cfrac{1}{1.2 + \cfrac{1}{2.3 + \cfrac{1}{13/5}}}$

3. a) 7, 22/3, 117/16, 841/115

   b) -3, -38/13, -79/27, -986/337, -4023/1395

4. a) 1, 3/2, 10/7, 43/30, 225/157

   b) -1, -2/3, -5/7, -82/115

   c) 0, 1/721

   d) 3, 3.833333, 3.611702, 3.635932

5. [2, 4, 4, 4, 4, ...]. The 4 repeats. The value x of this continued fraction satisfies $x = 2 + 1/(x + 2)$ which simplifies to $x^2 = 5$. Convergents and differences are

2/1	-0.236
9/4	0.014
38/17	-0.00077
161/72	0.000043
682/305	-0.0000024
2889/1292	0.00000013

6. $h_1 = 1$, $h_2 = q_2 > 0$, and for $i > 2$,

   $h_i = h_{i-2} + h_{i-1}q_i > h_{i-2}$

7. Step 1: $h_{-1}k_0 - k_{-1}h_0 = 1 \cdot 1 - 0 \cdot 0 = 1 = (-1)^0$

   Step 2: The formula shows that each of these terms is the negative of the previous one.

8. [1, 1, 2, 1, 2, 1, 2, 1, ...] . The 2,1 pattern repeats. The value xz of this continued fraction satisfies $x = 1 + 1/(1 + 1/(x + 1))$, which simplifies to $x^2 = 3$.

Convergents and differences are

1	-0.732
2	0.268
5/3	-0.065
7/4	0.018
19/11	-0.005
26/15	0.0013

9. $x = (3 + \sqrt{13})/2$ Convergents are 3, 10/3, 33/10, 109/33, 360/109, 1189/360.

10. $3x^2 - 9x + 5 = 0$; $x = (9 + \sqrt{21})/6 = 2.26376$; convergents are 2, 7/3, 9/4, 34/15, 43/19, 163/72.

11. 2, 3, 8/3, 11/4, 19/7, 87/32

Chapter Review

1. b, c

2. a) 1 b) 5 c) 1 d) 7 e) 1 f) 1

3. a) $2\cdot3\cdot5\cdot7\cdot11\cdot123$ b) $2^2\cdot3\cdot5^2\cdot7\cdot11^2\cdot13$

   c) $2\cdot7^2\cdot11^2$ d) $2^7\cdot3^3$

   e) $2\cdot5^5\cdot3^2$ f) $5\cdot997$

4. a) g.c.d = 5; l.c.m = 56,081,250

   b) g.c.d. = 154; l.c.m = 21,878,010

5. a) 64 b) 216 c) 18 d) 32 e) 36 f) 4

6. a) 857,088 b) 12,929,728 c) 22,743

   d) 10,200 e) 152,334 f) 5,988

7. a) $x = 2 - 12t$; $y = t$ b) $x = 21 + 48t$; $y = 24 + 55t$

   c) $x = 39 + 45t$; $y = 852 + 983t$

8. a) $x = 181 + 585t$; $y = 56 + 181t$ b) None

   c) $x = -13 + 37t$; $y = 26 - 75t$

9. [1], [3], [5], [9], [11], [13]

10. [1], [5], [11], [13], [17], [19], [23], [25], [29], [31], [37], [41]

11. [9]

12. [25]

13. a) $x = 2$, $y = 0$ b) As given above, with $t \geq 0$.

c) As given above, with $t \geq 0$.

d) As given above, with $t \geq 0$.

14. a) 1 b) 4 c) 1 d) 1

15. 9 NAND gates and 5 inverters

16. In 35 days.

17. Every 379.195 seconds.

18. In 896 days.

19. a) [-1, 2, 8, 2] b) [5, 7, 9, 11, 13]

20. a) $$2 + \cfrac{1}{8 + \cfrac{1}{2 + \cfrac{1}{8}}}$$ b) $$7 + \cfrac{1}{9}$$

b) $$2 + \cfrac{1}{1 + \cfrac{1}{1 + \cfrac{1}{1 + \cfrac{1}{4 + \cfrac{1}{1}}}}}$$ b) $$0 + \cfrac{1}{1 + \cfrac{1}{2 + \cfrac{1}{3 + \cfrac{1}{2 + \cfrac{1}{1}}}}}$$

21. a) -1, -1/2, -9/17, -19/36

b) 5, 36/7, 329/64, 3655/711, 47844/9307

22. a) 2, 17/8, 36/17, 305/144

b) 7, 64/9

c) 2, 3, 5/2, 8/3, 37/14, 45/17

d) 0, 1, 2/3, 7/10, 16/23, 23/33

23. [2, 2, 4, 2, 4, 2, ...]. The pattern 2,4 repeats. The value x of this continued fraction satisfies $x = 2 + 1/(2 + 1/(x + 2))$ which simplifies to $x^2 = 6$. Convergents and differences are

2	-0.45
5/2	0.05
22/9	-0.005
49/20	0.0005
218/89	-0.00005
485/198	0.000005

24. [3, 3, 6, 3, 6, 3, ...]. The pattern 3,6 repeats. The value x of this continued fraction satisfies $x = 3 + 1/(3 + 1/(x + 3))$ which simplifies to $x^2 = 11$. Convergents and differences are

3	-0.317
10/3	0.017
63/19	-0.00083
199/60	0.000041
1257/379	-0.000002
3970/1197	0.0000001

25. $x = 1 + \sqrt{2}/2$

1, 2, 5/3, 12/7, 29/17, 70/41

26. [1, 3, 1, 5, 1, 1,]

1, 4/3, 5/4, 29/23, 34/27, 63/50

Chapter 11

Section 11.1

1. For instance, aa, bb, aab, bba

2. a) a, b, a+, #b, etc.

   b) { a, aa }; { a, +, a+ }; { s | s is a string of a's }

3. a) Sentence = noun phrase verb object; noun phrase = "the" noun , or "the" noun prepositional phrase; prepositional phrase = preposition noun phrase.

   b) The manager made the decision.

   The manager of the supervisor made the decision.

   The manager of the supervisor of the leader of the project made the decision.

4. For instance, translate the answer to problem 3 into any language.

5. a) noun phrase, verb in past tense, object

   b) object, "was", verb in past tense, "by", subject

   c) See b).

6. Optional sign, zero or more digits , optional decimal point, additional digits, optional exponent consisting of E followed by optional sign followed by one or more digits.

7. a) BASIC: each statement is a separate line. Pascal: separated by semicolon; C: each statement ends in semicolon.

   b) BASIC: REM statement. Pascal: enclosed in { ... }. C: enclosed in /* ... */.

   c) BASIC: none (except in some dialects). Pascal: enclosed in begin...end. C: enclosed in (...)

Section 11.2

1. Any number of x's followed by one y.

2. Any possibly empty string of a's and b's followed by a c.

3. Any possibly empty string of a's and b's, followed by the same string in reverse order.

4. A non-empty string of x's followed by a string of y's, in which the number of x's is equal to or one greater than the number of y's.

5.

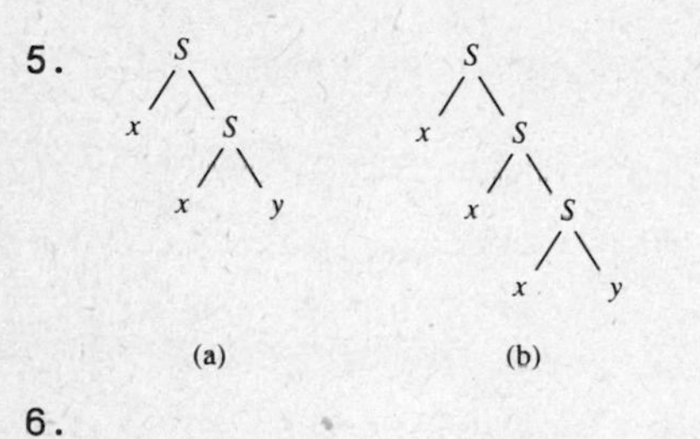

6.

(a)

S a S a b S b ∅

(b)

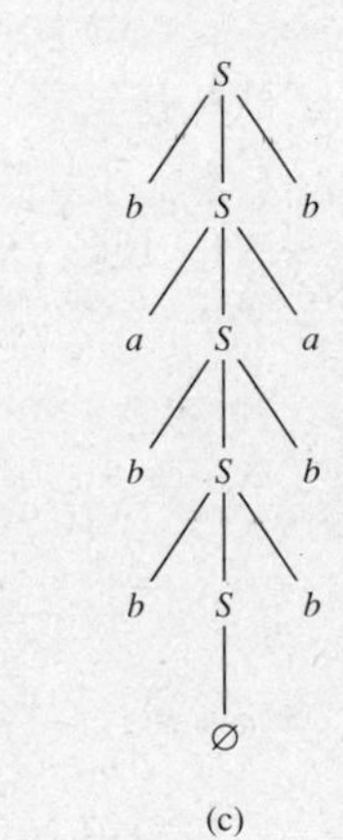

(c)

7.

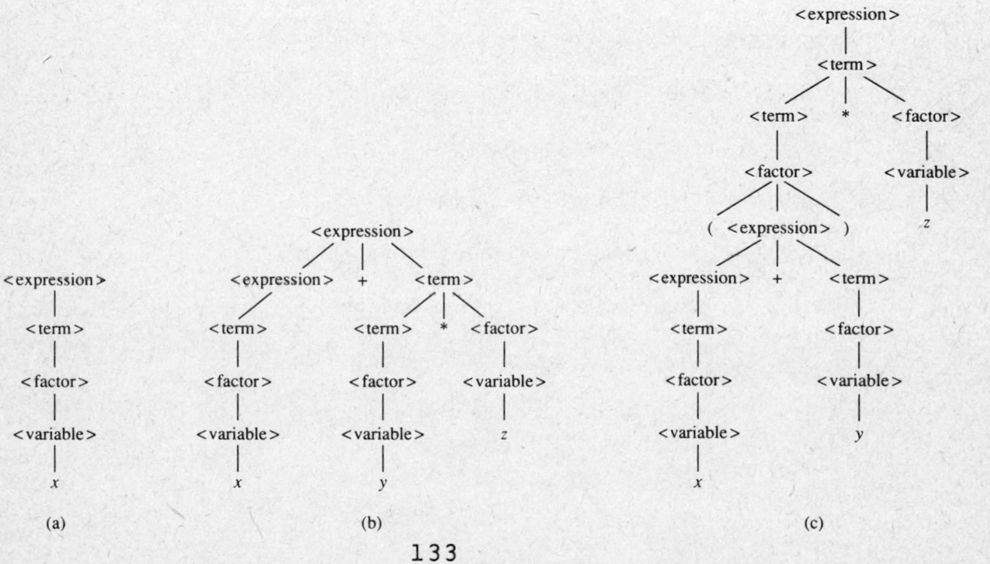

8. S ::= <empty> | xxS

9. S ::= x | xT

T ::= <empty> | xxT

10. S ::= <noun phrase> <transitive verb> <noun phrase>

<noun phrase> ::= <article> <noun> |

<article> <noun> <prepositional phrase>

<prepositional phrase> ::= <preposition> <noun phrase>

<article> ::= the | a

<noun> ::= cat | dog | dogcatcher | mathematics

<preposition> ::= of | by | on | under

<transitive verb> ::= runs | chases | studies

The dog chases the dogcatcher.

A cat studies the mathematics.

The mathematics under the dog runs a cat.

11. <number> ::= <sign> <simple number> <exponent>

<sign> ::= <empty> | + | -

<simple number> ::= <integer> | <integer>. | .<integer>

| <integer>.<integer>

<integer> ::= <digit> | <integer> <digit>

<digit> ::= 0 | 1 | 2 | 3 | 4 | 5 | 6 | 7 | 8 | 9

<exponent> ::= E <sign> <integer>

12. Replace definition of <factor> with

<factor> ::= <item> | <item> ** <factor>

<item> ::= <variable> | (<expression>)

13. S ::= AX | YC

Y ::= ab | aYb

A ::= a | aA

B ::= c | Cc

X ::= bc | bXc

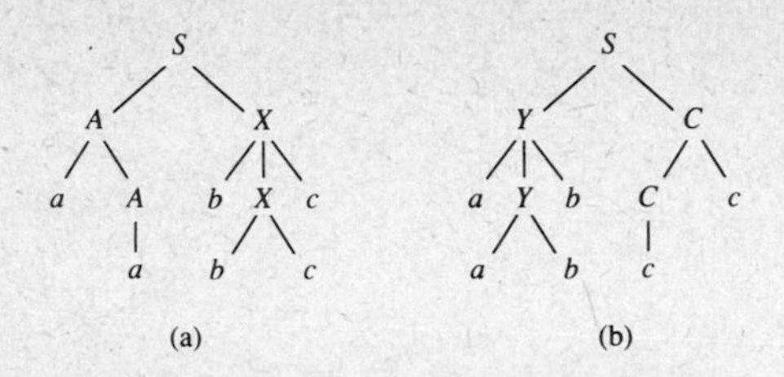

14. <expression> ::= <variable> |

- <expression>

+ <expression> <expression>

- <expression> <expression>

* <expression> <expression>

/ <expression> <expression>

The expression --xy is ambiguous, meaning either -(x-y) or (-x)-y. It is necessary to use different symbols for unary and binary -.

15. <expression> ::= <number> ENTR |

<expression> <number> <binary operator>

<expression> <expression> <binary operator>

<number> ±

<expression> ±

<binary operator> ::= + | - | * | /

Section 11.3

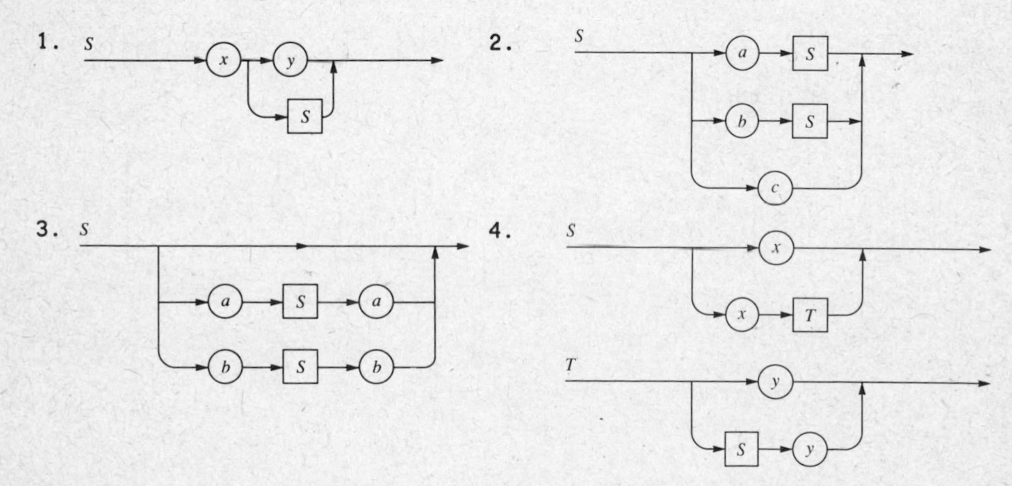

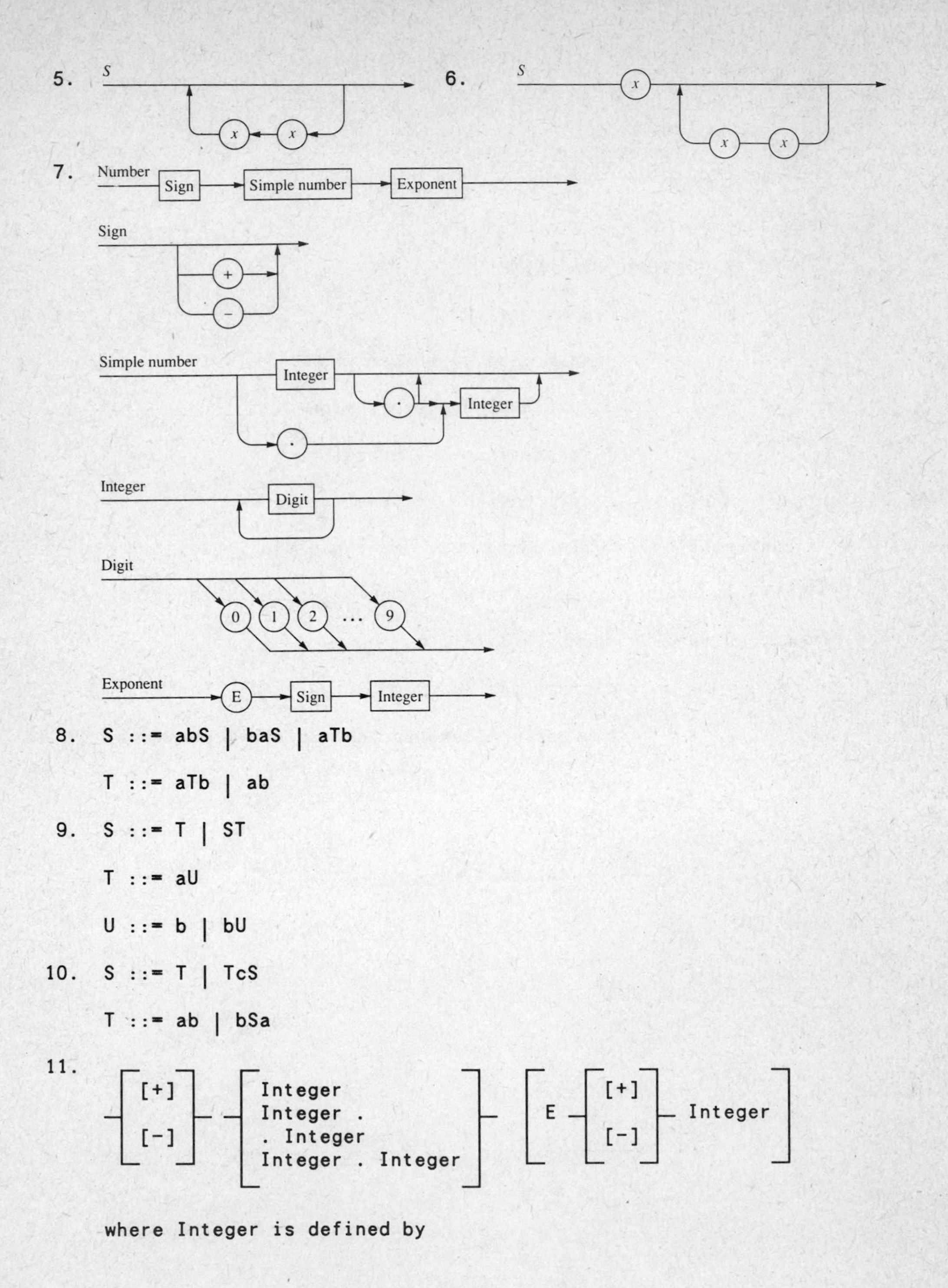

8. S ::= abS | baS | aTb

T ::= aTb | ab

9. S ::= T | ST

T ::= aU

U ::= b | bU

10. S ::= T | TcS

T ::= ab | bSa

11.

```
 ┌ [+] ┐   ┌ Integer                    ┐   ┌ E ─┌ [+] ┐─ Integer ┐
─┤     ├─ ─┤ Integer .                  ├─  │    │     │          │
 └ [-] ┘   │ . Integer                  │   └    └ [-] ┘          ┘
           └ Integer . Integer          ┘
```

where Integer is defined by

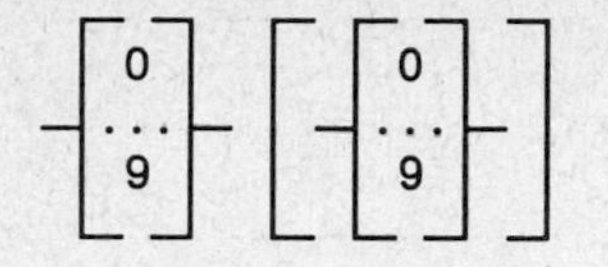


```
12.  S ::= "IDENTIFICATION DIVISION.
              PROGRAM-ID." A B C D E F
     A ::= <empty> | <character>A
     B ::= <empty> | "AUTHOR." A
     C ::= <empty> | "INSTALLATION." A
     D ::= <empty> | "DATE-WRITTEN." A
     E ::= <empty> | "DATE-COMPILED." A
     F ::= <empty> | "SECURITY." A
```

13. 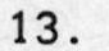

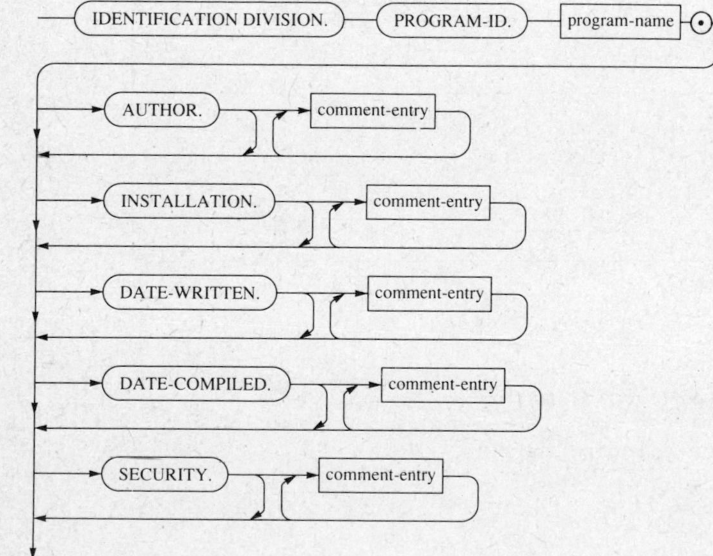


```
14.  S ::= "WRITE" A B C D
     A ::= <identifier>
     B ::= <empty> | "FROM" <identifier>
     C ::= <empty> | G H I
     D ::= <empty> | J K <imperative statement>
     G ::= <empty> | "BEFORE" | "AFTER"
```

```
H ::= <empty> | "ADVANCING"

I ::= <identifier> "LINE" | <identifier> "LINES" |
      <integer> "LINE" | <integer> "LINES" |
      <mnemonic-name> | "PAGE"

J ::= <empty> | "AT"

K ::= "END-OF-PAGE" | "EOP"
```

15. 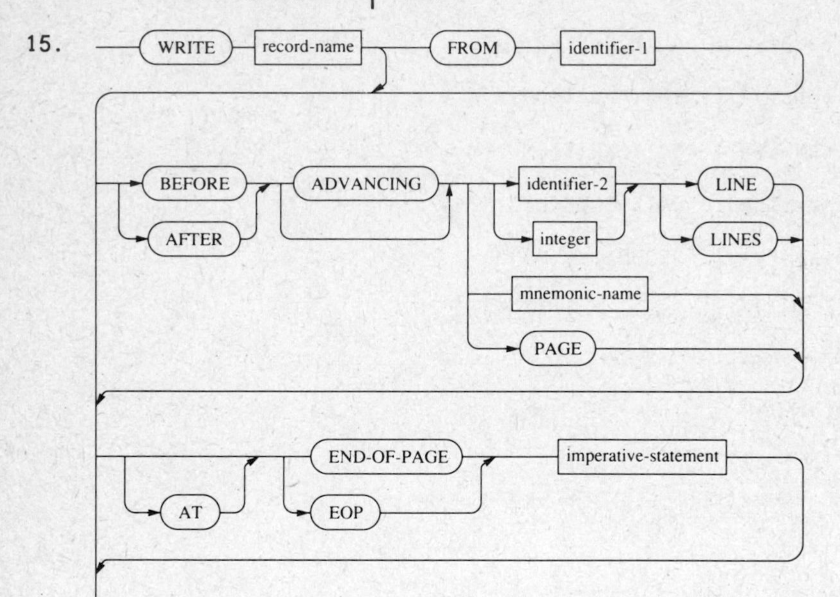

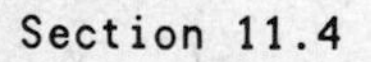

Section 11.4

1. a) predicate logic, math

   b) predicate logic, math

   c) none

2. a) none

   b) propositional logic, predicate logic, math

   c) math

3. a) $z \notin x \vee z \in y$

   b) $w \in x \wedge x \subseteq y \Rightarrow w \in y$

4. $x \subset y \wedge y \subseteq z \Rightarrow x \subseteq z$

Chapter Review

1. Noun phrase, verb, object; where a noun phrase is either a noun (optionally preceeded by an article or an adjective), an infinitive, or a gerund; an infinitive is the word "to" followed by a verb; object is an adjective or a noun phrase; and a gerund is a verb with "ing" attached followed by a noun phrase.
2. Alternating a's and b's, beginning with a.
3. A string of x's with one b at either end.
4. A possibly empty string of a's followed by a string of b's, where the number of a's is less than or equal to the number of b's.
5. S ::= xxS | xyE | yxE | yyS

   E ::= xxE | xyS | yxS | yyE | <empty>
6. S : XYX

   X ::= <empty> | xX

   Y ::= <empty> | yY
7.

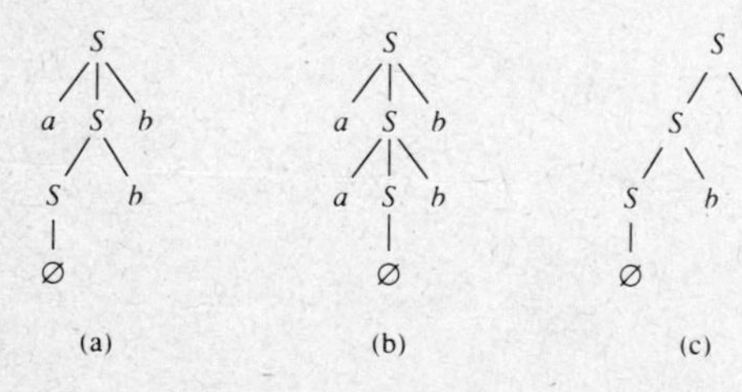

(a) (b) (c)

8.

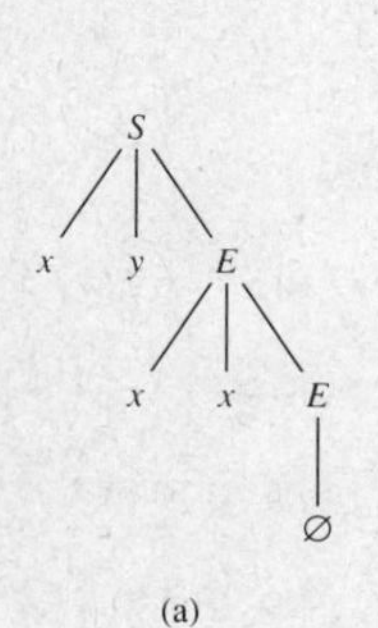

(a)

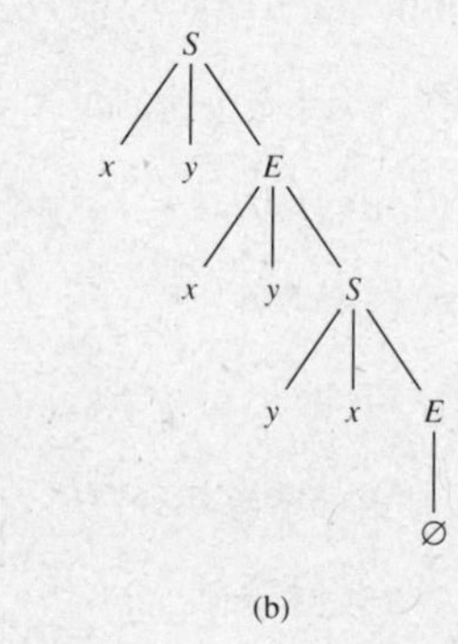

(b)

9.

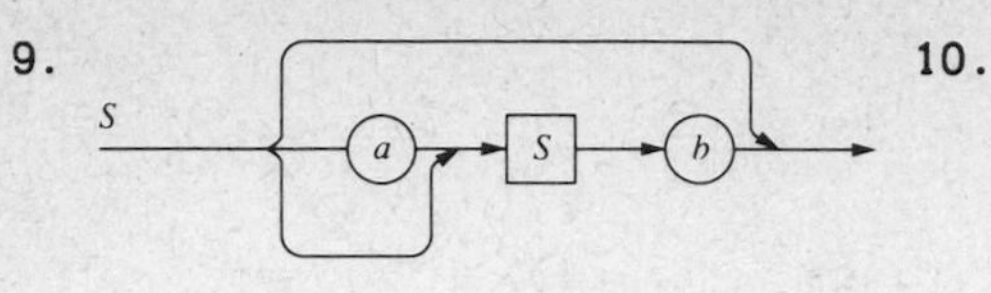

10.

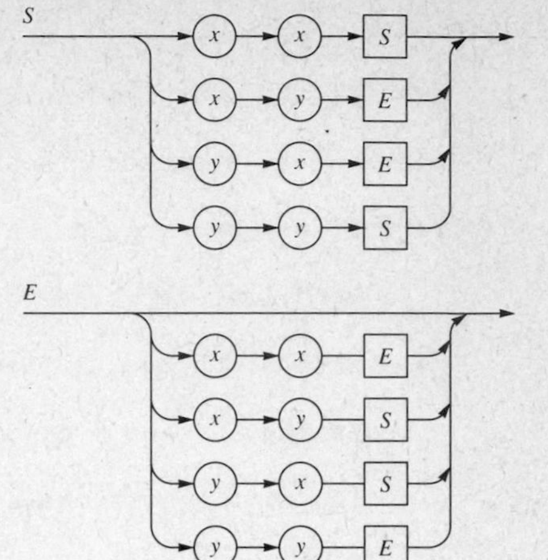

11. S ::= T | ST

    T ::= a | abT

12. S ::= xTa | yTa | xTb | yTb

    T ::= bSy | c

13.

$$\left[\begin{array}{l} \text{b x [x]...} \\ \text{x [x]... b} \end{array}\right]$$

14. [x]...[y]...[x]...

Chapter 12

Section 12.1

1. 2^{32} = 4,294,967,296

2. The printable characters and as many control characters as can be generated at the keyboard.

3. Printable characters, carriage return, line feed.

4. A fixed disk drive is an extension of the computer's memory and so increases the number of available states. A removable disk can be considered a tape, if the operator has an infinite number of disks available. Other output devices are equivalent to printers or tapes.

Section 12.2

1. a) U, V, V, V

   b) U, T, T, V

   c) V, V, V

2. a) T, V, T, T, V, T, U

   b) T, T, V, V, V, V, T

   c) T, T, T, T, T, T, V

3. Input alphabet = { nickel, dime, quarter }

   States = { I, S5, S10, S15 }

   Initial state = I

4. a) S5, S10, S15, I, S5

   b) I, S5, I, S5, S15

5. a) S10, I, S10, I, S5

   b) S5, S15, I, S10, S15, I, S5

6.

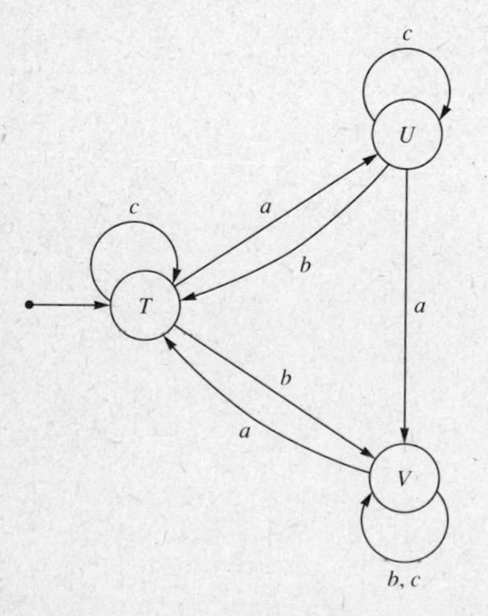

7.

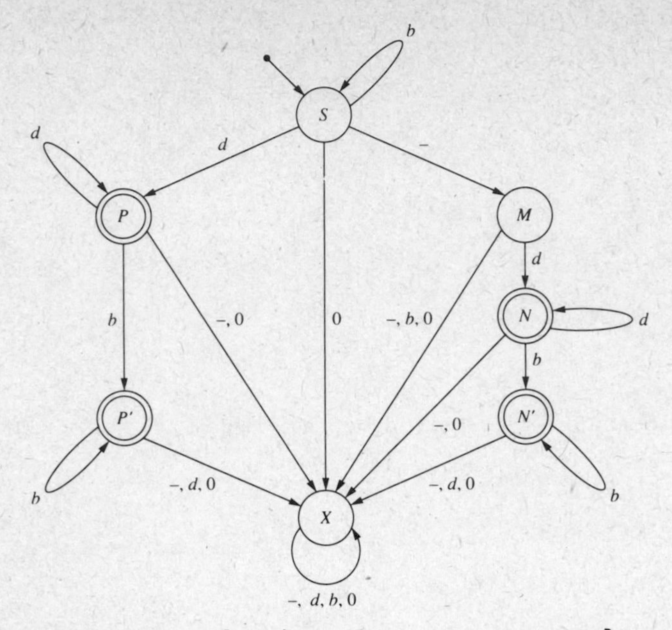

8. a) Input alphabet = { undercurrent, overcurrent }

States = { good, blown }

Initial state = good

Transition function:

	undercurrent	overcurrent
good	good	blown
blown	blown	blown

b) Input alphabet =

{ undercurrent, overcurrent, turn on, turn off }

States = { on, off, tripped }

Initial state = on

Transition function:

	under	over	turn on	turn off
on	on	tripped	on	off
off	off	off	on	off
tripped	tripped	tripped	tripped	off

c) Input alphabet = { 0, 1, 2, 3, 4, 5, 6, 7, 8, 9, Cancel, Start, Tick } The states include Off; for each time t in $0 \le t \le T$, a state N_t in which the oven is not operating , and the time shown on the display is t, and for each t, a state O_t in which the time remaining is t. The initial state is Off. The transition function is:

	0 ... 9	Cancel	Start	Tick
Off	Note 1	Off	Off	Off
N_t	Note 1	Off	O_t	N_t
O_t (t > 0)	O_t	Off	O_t	O_{t-1}
O_0	O_0	Off	O_0	Off

Note 1: New state is $N_{t'}$, where t' is the time obtained from t by adding the entered digit on the right.

9. a) Input alphabet = { 1, 2, 3, 4, 5, 6, 7, 8, 9, Burglary }

States = { Armed (A), A5, A54, A542, Disarmed (D), D7, Alarm (L), L5, L54, L542 }

Transition function:

	1	2	3	4	5	6	7	8	9	B
A	A	A	A	A	A5	A	A	A	A	L
A5	A	A	A	A54	A	A	A	A	A	L
A54	A	A542	A	A	A	A	A	A	A	L
A542	A	A	A	A	A	A	D	A	A	L
D	D	D	D	D	D	D	D7	D	D	D
D7	D	D	D	D	D	D	D	D	A	D
L	L	L	L	L	L5	L	L	L	L	L
L5	L	L	L	L54	L	L	L	L	L	L
L54	L	L542	L	L	L	L	L	L	L	L
L54	L	L	L	L	L	L	D	L	L	L

b) Input alphabet = { SToP, PLaY, RECord, Fast Forward, REWind, PAUse, Beginning of Tape, End of Tape }

States = { SToP, PLaY, RECord, Fast Forward, REWind, PAUse-Play, PAUse-Record }

	STP	PLY	REC	FF	REW	PAU	BOT	EOT
STP	STP	PLY	REC	FF	REW	STP	STP	STP
PLY	STP	PLY	PLY	FF	REW	PAUP	PLY	STP
REC	STP	REC	REC	FF	REW	PAUR	REC	STP
FF	STP	PLY	REC	FF	REW	STP	FF	STP
REW	STP	PLY	REC	FF	REW	STP	STP	REW
PAUP	STP	PAUP	PAUP	FF	REW	PLY	PAUP	STP
PAUR	STP	PAUR	PAUR	FF	REW	REC	PAUR	STP

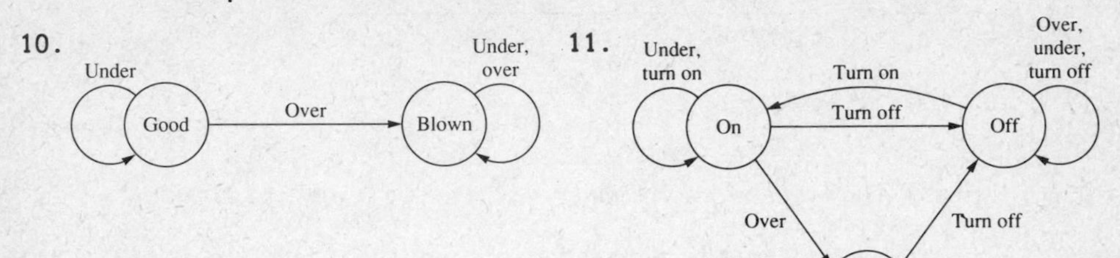

Section 12.3

1. a) SA　　b) SAT

   b) SBT　　d) SAA'T

2. a) SATTT　　b) SDTT

   c) SAT　　d) STT

3. a) SA　　b) SAS

   c) SASAT　　d) SASASAS

   e) SASASASE　　f) STTTTTTT

4. a) EEEFEEFFE　　b) EFEEFFEEF

   b) EEFEFEFFE　　d) FFFFFFFFFFEF

5. a) SABSDSD; Accepted　　b) SABSABSDSD; Accepted

   c) SABSDS; Not accepted　　d) SDSABTT; Not accepted

6. The sequences abc and de repeated any number of times in any order, followed by d. Infinite because the loops SaAbBcS and SdDeS are loops in paths to an accepting state.

7. a) SAE; Accepted　　b) SBE; Accepted

c) SAED; Not accepted d) SBEC; Not accepted

e) SBECDCDC; Not accepted f) SADCDCD; Not accepted

8. { aa, ac, ba, bc, ca, cb } Finite because the only loop in the diagram, D ⟷ C, is not in a path to an accepting state.

9.

(a)

(b)

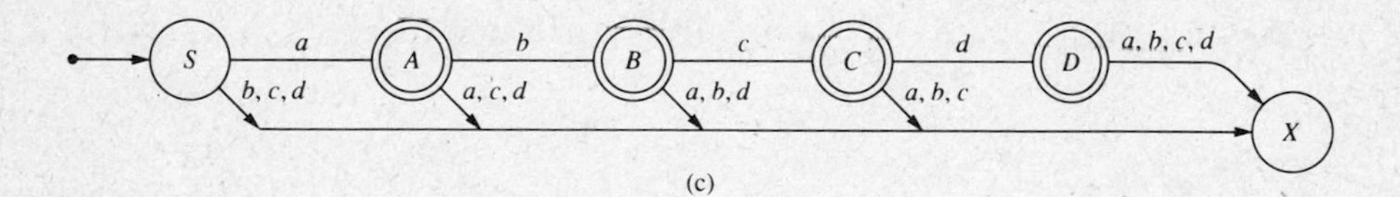

(c)

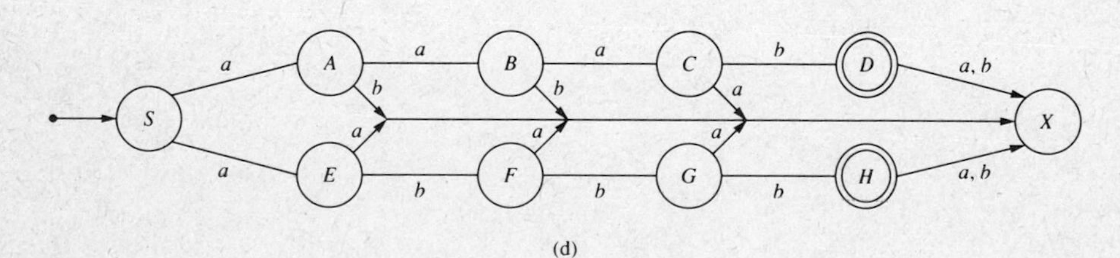

(d)

10.

	a	b
S	A	S
A	B	A
B	C	B
C	C	C

S is start state
C is accepting state

11. a) SAB b) SAABBC

c) SSSAAB c) SSSAAABBBCC

12.

	0	1
EE	OE	EO
EO	OO	EE
OE	EE	OO
OO	EO	OE

EE is start state
EO is accepting state

13. a) EE, EO, OO, OE, EE, EO, OO

b) EE, EO, EE, EO, OO, EO

c) EE, OE, EE, EO, EE, OE

d) EE, EO, EE, OE, OO, EO, OO

14.

	a	b	c
S	SA	X	X
SA	MA	MAB	AC
MA	MA	MAB	X
MAB	X	X	X
AC	X	X	ACC
ACC	X	X	ACCC
ACCC	X	X	X
X	X	X	X

S is start state
MAB and ACCC
are accepting states

15. a) S, SA, AC, ACC

b) S, SA, MA, MA, MA, MAB

c) S, SA, MAB, X, X

d) S, SA, AC, X

Section 12.4

1. S ::= aE | bE | a | b

E ::= aS | bE | b

2.

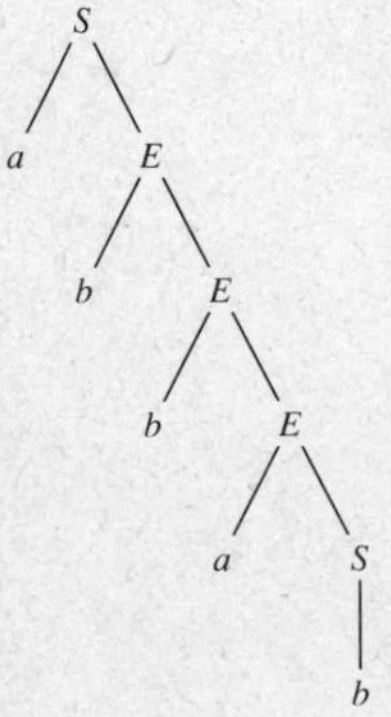

(a)

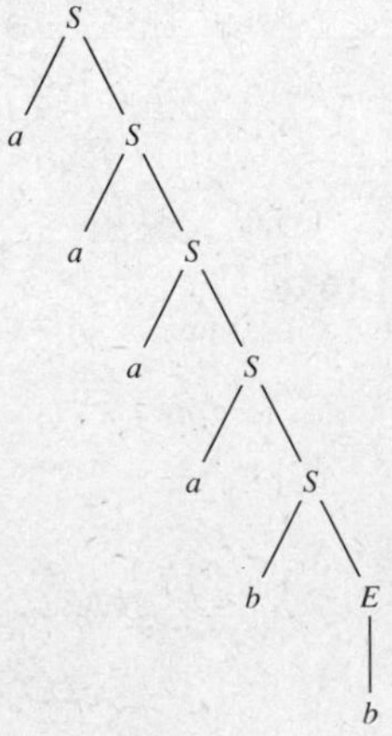

(b)

3.

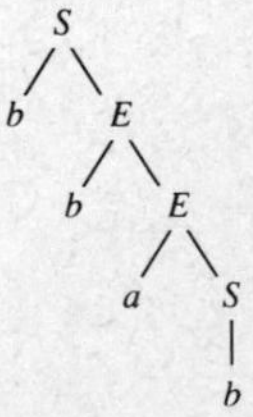

(a)

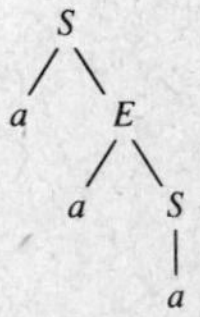

(b)

4. S ::= aA | bB

A ::= aB | bS | b

B ::= aB | bS | b

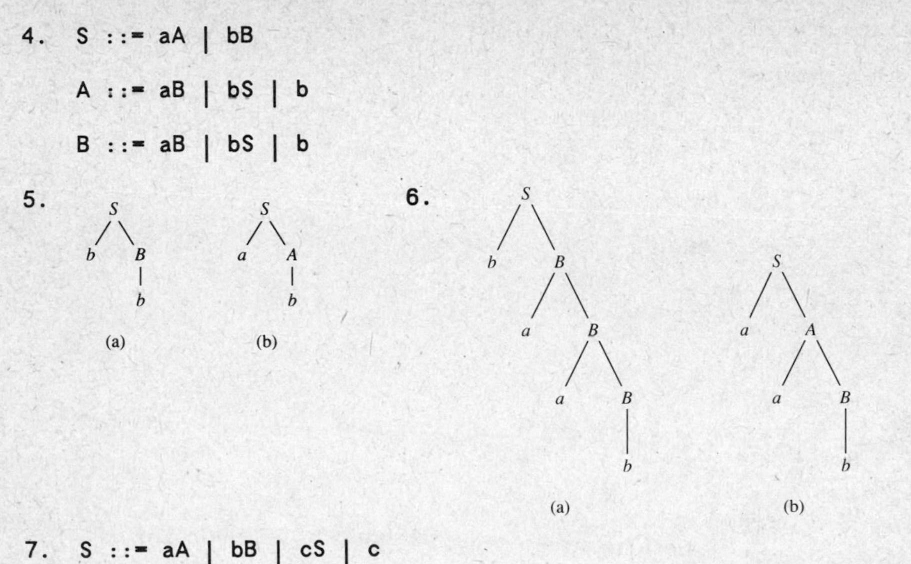

(a) (b) (a) (b)

7. S ::= aA | bB | cS | c

A ::= aA | bS | b | cB

B ::= aS | a | bB | cA

8. S ::= aA | a

A ::= bB

B ::= aA | a

9. S ::= aA | dD | d

A ::= bB

B ::= cS

D ::= eS

10. S ::= aA | bA | cB

A ::= a | c

B ::= a | b

Section 12.5

1. a) S ::= aA | a | c

A ::= cB

B ::= bS

b) S ::= cA | aC | b

```
    A ::= aB
    B ::= cS
    C ::= cD
    D ::= aS
 c) S ::= aC | bD | a
    B ::= aE | bC
    C ::= bB
    D ::= aS
    E ::= aG
    G ::= aS
2. a) S ::= aC | cS | a
    B ::= cS | a
    C ::= bD
    D ::= bB
 b) S ::= bC | bD | bE | c
    C ::= aS
    D ::= aF
    F ::= c
    E ::= aG
    G ::= aS
```

3. a) { S, E } b) { S }

   c) { S } d) { S }

4. a) ϕ b) ϕ

   c) ϕ d) ϕ

5.

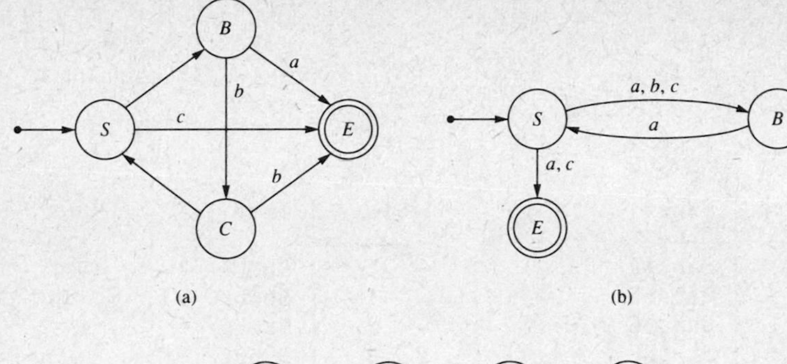

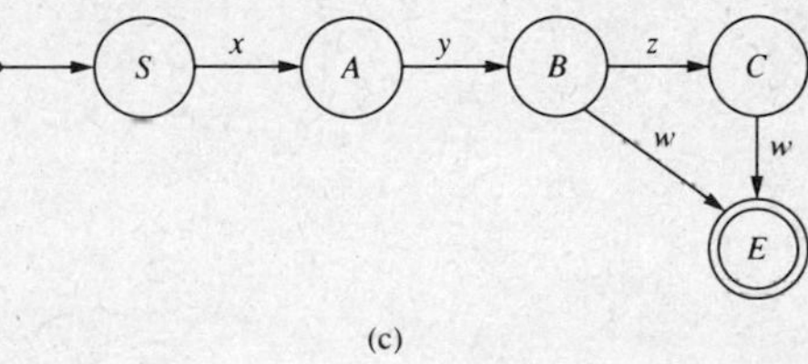

(c)

Section 12.6

1. a)

State	Tape
1	ababc
1	bbabc
1	bcabc
1	bcbbc
1	bcbcc
2	bcbcc
2	bcbac
H	bcaac

b)

State	Tape
1	ccbbaa
2	ccbbaa
2	acbbaa
2	acbbaa
etc.	

2. a)

State	Tape
1	cbaaccccb
2	cbaaccccb
2	abaaccccb
2	abaaccccb
etc.	

b)

State	Tape
1	bcabcabca
1	ccabcabca
2	ccabcabca
2	acabcabca
2	acabcabca
etc.	

3.

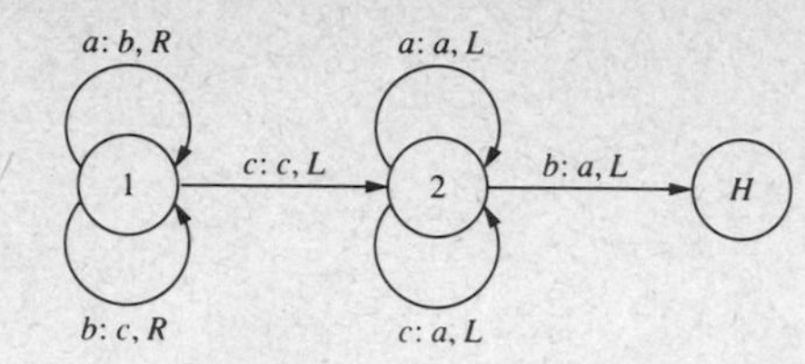

4. a)

State	Tape
1	BababE
1	BababE
2	BxbabE
4	BxxabE
4	BxxabE
1	BxxabE
1	BxxabE
1	BxxabE
2	BxxxbE
4	BxxxxE
4	BxxxxE
4	BxxxxE
4	BxxxxE
1	BxxxxE
1	BxxxxE
1	BxxxxE
1	BxxxxE
1	BxxxxE
H	BxxxxY

b)

State	Tape
1	BbbbE
1	BbbbE
3	BxbbE
3	BxbbE
3	BxbbE
H	BxbbN

5.

Symbols

States	BOT	a	b	x	EOI
0	(BOT,R,1)	(a,R,0)	(b,R,0)	(x,R,0)	(EOI,R,0)
1	(BOT,R,1)	(x,R,2)	(x,R,3)	(x,R,1)	(Y,-,H)
2	---------	(a,R,2)	(x,L,4)	(x,R,2)	(N,-,H)
3	---------	(x,L,4)	(b,R,3)	(x,R,3)	(N,-,H)
4	(BOT,R,1)	(a,L,4)	(b,L,4)	(x,L,4)	-------

6.

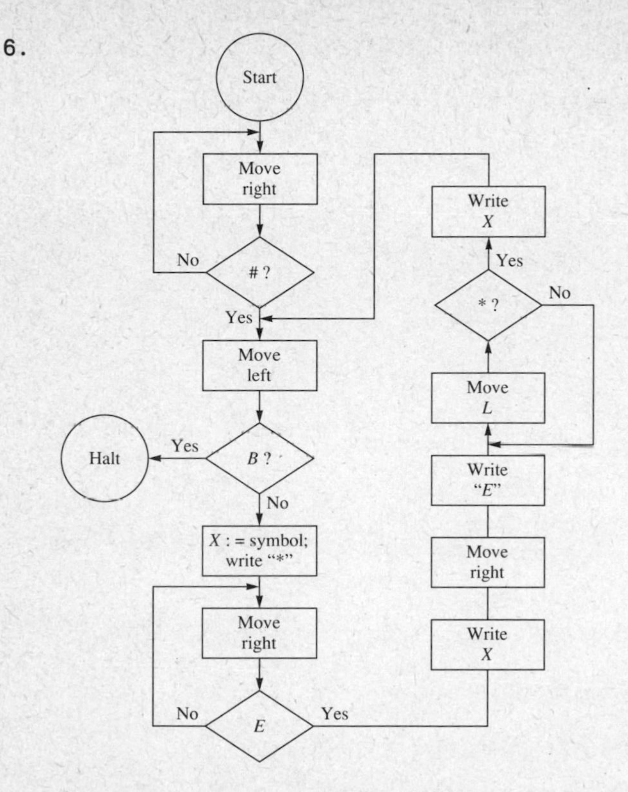

7. Represent two tapes (A and B) on one tape by putting tape A contents in even-numbered cells and tape B contents in odd-numbered cells. For each tape, introduce a "current location" marker into the alphabet. The machine must store in a memory the "true" contents of the positions occupied by the current location markers, and whether the current location is to the left or right of each marker. (Adding k bits of memory to a Turing machine is equivalent to multiplying the number of states by 2^k.) To do an operation on either tape, the machine must search for the current location marker, replace it with the true contents, modify the tape, note the contents of the new position, and rewrite the current location marker.

8. Let k be an integer $\geq \log_2(N)$; then each character in A can be

represented by k bits. To read a character of A, the machine must read k bits (this adds k bits to the machine's memory), then backspace over them. To write a character, write k bits. Additional memory is required to count the bits in the read, backspace, and write operations.

Section 12.7

1.

	x
1	x, R, 1

2.

	1	0
1	1,R,H	0,R,2
2	1,R,H	0,R,3
3	1,R,H	0,R,4
4	1,R,H	0,R,5
5	1,R,5	0,R,5

3. F("BOT",1)=("BOT",R,1);F("BOT",2)=("BOT",R,1);

   F("BOT",3)=("BOT",R,1);F("BOT",4)=("BOT",R,1);

   F("a",1)=("x",R,2);F("b",1)=("x",R,3);F("x",1)=("x",R,1);

   F("a",2)=("a",R,2);F("b",2)=("x",L,4);F("x",2)=("x",R,2);

   F("a",3)=("x",L,4);F("b",3)=("b",R,3);F("x",3)=("x",R,3);

   F("a",4)=("a",L,4);F("b",4)=("b",L,4);F("x",4)=("x",L,4);

   F("EOI",1)=("Y",R,H);F("EOI",2)=("N",R,H);

   F("EOI",3)=("N",R,H);F("EOI",4)=("N",R,H).BaabE

4. F("x",1)=("x",R,1).

5. F("1",1)=("1",R,H);F("0",1)=("0",R,2);

   F("1",2)=("1",R,H);F("0",2)=("0",R,3);

   F("1",3)=("1",R,H);F("0",3)=("0",R,4);

   F("1",4)=("1",R,H);F("0",4)=("0",R,5);

   F("1",5)=("1",R,5);F("0",5)=("0",R,5).00101101

6. S ::= . | F(" A

A ::= <symbol>", B

B ::= <digit>B | <digit>C

C ::=)=(" D

D ::= <symbol>", E

E ::= R, G | L, G

G ::= <digit> G | <digit> I | H I

I ::=); S |).

Chapter Review

1. The operator of a terminal can change the input sequence in response to the output, which is impossible with an abstract tape.

2. a) SASSSSBSA; Not accepted.

   b) SSBSSBSSS; Accepted

   c) SBBBBBBBB; Not accepted

   d) SAAAAAAAS; Accepted

3. a) SABABABABA; Accepted

   b) STTTTTTTTTT; Not accepted

   c) SATTTTTTTT; Not accepted

   d) STTTTTTTTT; Not accepted

4. There are four states: Neither, CAPS, NUM, and Both. Inputs include striking CAPS LOCK, NUM LOCK, letter keys, keypad keys, and other keys. CAPS LOCK and NUM LOCK change the machine state and produce null output. Other keys leave the state unchange; the outputs for the other keys are unchanged or change depending on the state.

5. a) 1) SABSABSABSA   2) STTTT

   3) SABST   4) SABSABSTTTT

   b) S::= <empty> | a | ab | abcS

c) Any finite initial part of the string abcabc......

6. 

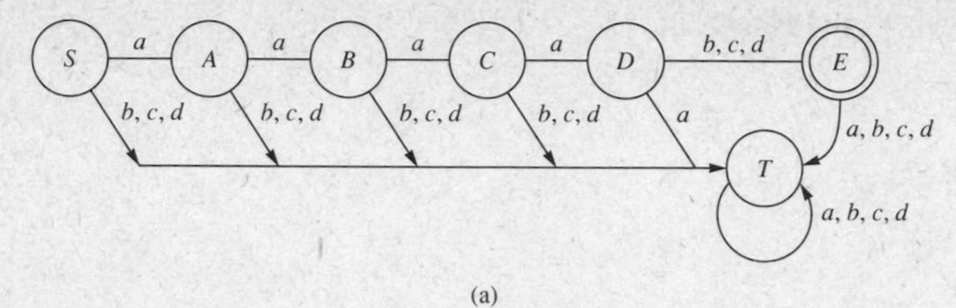

(a)

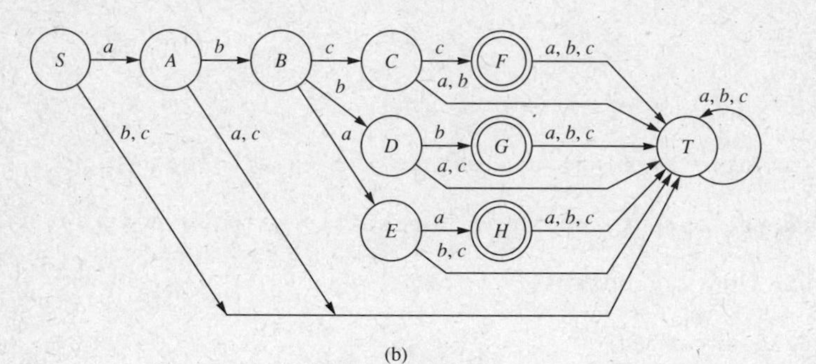

(b)

(c)

7. There are 64 states, corresponding to 0, 1, 2, or >2 a's, b's, and c's. The machine may be viewed as consisting of three counters. Encountering a letter increments the corresonding counter. The accepting states are those in which the value of at least one counter is 2.

8. a) 1) SASCSASCS   2) SSSSSASCS

   3) SASCCS   4) SCCSC

   b) S ::= <empty> eS | bS | dS | aA | cC | e | b | d

A ::= aA | bS | cA | dA | eA | b

C ::= aC | bC | cC | dS | eC | d

9. a) S ::= aA | bB | bC | a

A ::= bS

B ::= aD

D ::= cS

C ::= cS

b) S ::= aA | bT | bS

A ::= bT | bS

T ::= cT | aS | a

10.

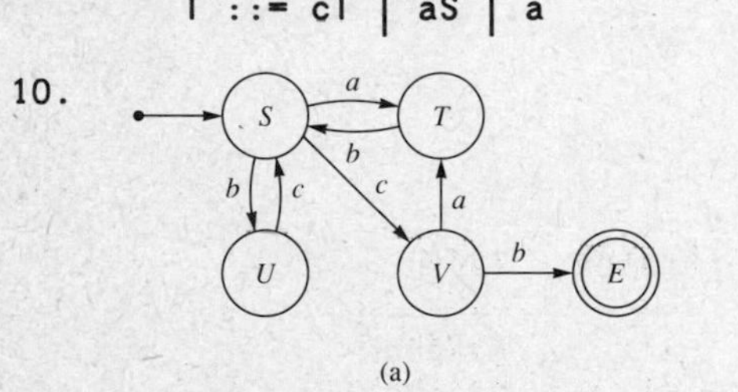

(a)

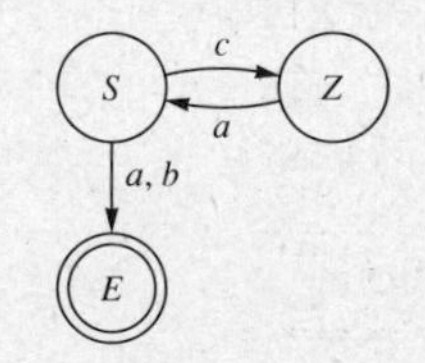

(b)

11.

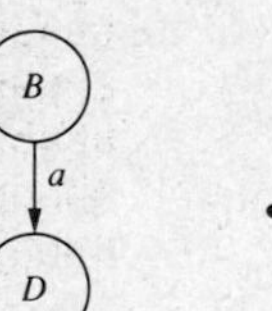

(a)

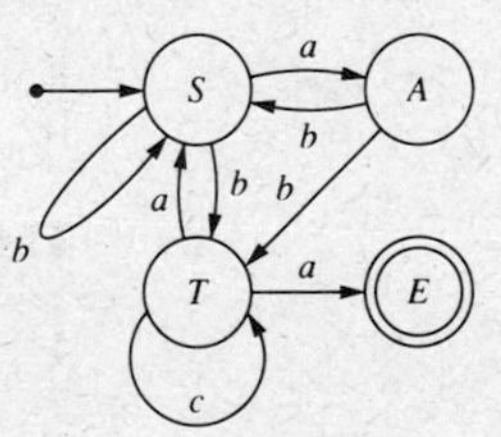

(b)

12.

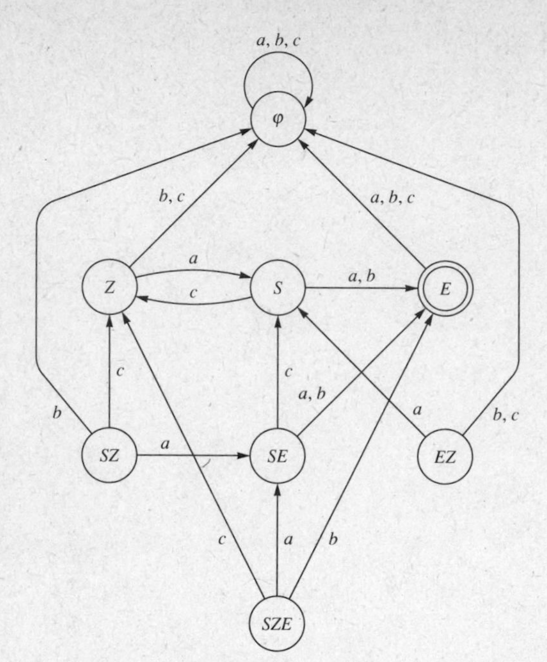

13. a)

States	Tape
1	aaaaa
1	baaaa
1	bbaaa
1	bbbaa
1	bbbba
1	bbbbb
H	bbbbba

b)

States	Tape
1	aaaabbb
1	baaabbb
1	bbaabbb
1	bbbabbb
1	bbbbbbb
2	bbbbbbb
H	bbbbbbb

c)

States	Tape
1	ababa
1	bbaba
2	bbaba
2	bbaba
H	bbaba

d)

States	Tape
1	bbbba
2	bbbba
H	bbbba